Advancing Maths for AQA
MECHANICS 2

Ted Graham and Aidan Burrows

Series editors
Ted Graham   Sam Boardman   Graham Eaton
Keith Parramore   Roger Williamson

Heinemann

Heinemann Educational Publishers
a division of Heinemann Publishers (Oxford) Ltd,
Halley Court, Jordan Hill, Oxford OX2 8EJ

OXFORD   MELBOURNE   AUCKLAND   JOHANNESBURG
BLANTYRE   GABORONE   PORTSMOUTH NH (USA)   CHICAGO

First published in 2001

01 10 9 8 7 6 5 4 3 2 1

ISBN 0 435 51307 9

Typeset and illustrated by Tech-Set Limited, Gateshead, Tyne & Wear

Printed and bound by Scotprint in the UK

Acknowledgements
The publishers and authors acknowledge the work of the writers, Ray Atkin,
John Berry, Derek Collins, Tim Cross, Ted Graham, Phil Rawlins, Tom Roper,
Rob Summerson, Nigel Price, Frank Chorlton and Andy Martin of the *AEB
Mathematics for AS* and *A-Level* Series, from which some exercises and examples
have been taken.

The publishers' and authors' thanks are due to the AQA for permission to
reproduce questions from past examination papers.

The answers have been provided by the authors and are not the responsibility
of the examining board.

About this book

This book is one in a series of textbooks designed to provide you with exceptional preparation for AQA's new Advanced GCE Specification B. The series authors are all senior members of the examining team and have prepared the textbooks specifically to support you in studying this course.

Finding your way around

The following are there to help you find your way around when you are studying and revising:
- **edge marks** (shown on the front page) – these help you to get to the right chapter quickly;
- **contents list** – this identifies the individual sections dealing with key syllabus concepts so that you can go straight to the areas that you are looking for;
- **index** – a number in bold type indicates where to find the main entry for that topic.

Key points

Key points are not only summarised at the end of each chapter but are also boxed and highlighted within the text like this:

$$v = \frac{dx}{dt}$$

The velocity is equal to the rate of change of the displacement.

Exercises and exam questions

Worked examples and carefully graded questions familiarise you with the specification and bring you up to exam standard. Each book contains:
- Worked examples and Worked exam questions to show you how to tackle typical questions; Examiner's tips will also provide guidance;
- Graded exercises, gradually increasing in difficulty up to exam-level questions, which are marked by an [A];
- Test-yourself sections for each chapter so that you can check your understanding of the key aspects of that chapter and identify any sections that you should review;
- Answers to the questions are included at the end of the book.

Kinematics and variable acceleration

Learning objectives

After studying this chapter you should be able to:

■ differentiate displacements or position vectors to give velocities and accelerations for one, two or three dimensions
■ integrate accelerations to give velocities and position vectors or displacements.

1.1 Introduction

In the M1 module you would have considered only cases where the acceleration of an object is constant. For example a ball falling under gravity or perhaps a car with a constant acceleration. However there are many situations where it is unrealistic to assume that the acceleration of a body is constant or where better solutions to problems can be obtained by modelling the acceleration as variable. For example circular motion involves an acceleration that is always changing direction and the acceleration of a car may decrease as it gains speed.

In some cases the acceleration can be expressed as a function of time, in others it may depend on the speed or velocity of the object under consideration. In this chapter you will consider cases where the acceleration is dependent on time, but in later chapters you will consider cases where the acceleration depends on displacement or velocity.

This chapter will require you to use calculus instead of the constant acceleration equations, from now on when approaching a problem it is important to decide whether or not the acceleration is constant before using the constant acceleration equations. In general you will find that there will be relatively little use of constant acceleration equations in this module.

1.2 Displacement to velocity and acceleration

In the M1 module it was noted that the velocity was given by the gradient of a displacement–time graph and that the acceleration was given by the gradient of a velocity–time graph. These results can be used as the basis of your work with variable acceleration.

The gradient of a curve is given by its derivative so we can deduce that the velocity is given by the derivative, with respect to time, of the displacement.

$$v = \frac{dx}{dt}$$

The velocity is equal to the rate of change of the displacement.

Similarly the acceleration will be given by the derivative of the velocity, with respect to time.

$$a = \frac{dv}{dt}$$

The acceleration is equal to the rate of change of the velocity.

You can also write

$$a = \frac{d^2x}{dt^2}.$$

The following worked examples illustrate how these results can be applied.

Worked example 1.1

The height of a bullet, h metres, fired vertically upwards, at time t seconds, is given by:

$$h = 3 + 80t - 4.9t^2$$

Show that the acceleration of the bullet is constant and find its maximum height.

Solution

First differentiate h to find the velocity.

$$v = \frac{dh}{dt}$$
$$= 80 - 2 \times 4.9t$$
$$= 80 - 9.8t$$

Now differentiate again to find the acceleration.

$$a = \frac{dv}{dt}$$

$$= -9.8$$

So the acceleration is constant and has magnitude 9.8 m s^{-2}.

The maximum height will be attained when the velocity is zero.

$$80 - 9.8t = 0$$

$$t = \frac{80}{9.8}$$

This can then be substituted into the expression for h to find the maximum height.

$$h = 3 + 80 \times \frac{80}{9.8} - 4.9 \times \left(\frac{80}{9.8}\right)^2$$

$$= 330 \text{ m (to 3 sf)}$$

This example shows that calculus can also be applied to cases involving constant acceleration.

Worked example 1.2

As a car slows down the distance, s metres, it has travelled at time t seconds is modelled by the equation:

$$s = \frac{t^4}{8} - t^3 + 16t + 32 \text{ for } 0 \leqslant t \leqslant 4.$$

(a) Show that when $t = 4$ the car has zero velocity.

(b) Find the acceleration, when $t = 0$, $t = 2$ and $t = 4$.

(c) Describe how the resultant force on the car changes.

Solution

(a) First you need to differentiate s to find an expression for the velocity.

$$v = \frac{ds}{dt}$$

$$= \frac{4t^3}{8} - 3t^2 + 16$$

$$= \frac{t^3}{2} - 3t^2 + 16$$

Now substitute $t = 4$ in this expression.

$$v = \frac{4^3}{2} - 3 \times 4^2 + 16$$

$$= 32 - 48 + 16$$

$$= 0$$

(b) Now differentiate again to find the acceleration.

$$a = \frac{dv}{dt}$$

$$= \frac{3t^2}{2} - 6t$$

Substituting the values $t = 0$, $t = 2$ and $t = 4$ gives

$$t = 0, a = \frac{3 \times 0^2}{2} - 6 \times 0 = 0 \text{ m s}^{-2}$$

$$t = 2, a = \frac{3 \times 2^2}{2} - 6 \times 2 = -6 \text{ m s}^{-2}$$

$$t = 4, a = \frac{3 \times 4^2}{2} - 6 \times 4 = 0 \text{ m s}^{-2}$$

(c) The acceleration is always negative, and varies as shown in the graph. Its magnitude increases from 0 m s^{-2} to 6 m s^{-2} and then decreases back to 0 m s^{-2} as the car comes to rest after 4 seconds.

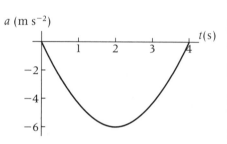

Worked example 1.3

A ball is released from rest at the top of a tall building and falls vertically. The distance fallen by the ball at time t seconds is x m where

$$x = 5t + 2.5e^{-2t} - 2.5$$

(a) Find an expression for the velocity and sketch a graph to show how the velocity varies with time.

(b) Find an expression for the acceleration and sketch a graph to show how this varies with time.

Solution

(a) Differentiate x with respect to t to find v.

$$v = \frac{dx}{dt}$$

$$= 5 - 5e^{-2t}$$

Initially v is 0, but increases to 5 m s^{-1} as t increases, as shown in the graph.

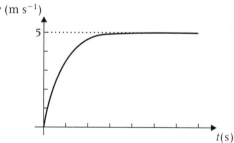

(b) Differentiating again gives the acceleration.

$$a = \frac{dv}{dt}$$

$$= 10e^{-2t}$$

Initially the acceleration is 10 m s^{-2}, but this decreases to 0 as shown in the graph.

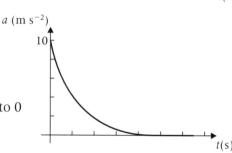

EXERCISE 1A

1 The distances, in metres, travelled by a cyclist after t seconds are given by

$$s = \frac{t^3}{6} - \frac{t^4}{120} \quad \text{for} \quad 0 \leqslant t \leqslant 10.$$

(a) How far has the cyclist travelled when $t = 10$.

(b) Find an expression for the velocity of the cyclist at time t.

(c) Find an expression for the acceleration of the cyclist at time t.

(d) Describe how the acceleration of the cyclist changes.

2 A car accelerates from rest so that the distance that it has travelled in t seconds is s metres where $s = t^2 - \frac{t^3}{60}$.

(a) Find expressions for the velocity and acceleration at time t seconds.

The expression for s is valid while the acceleration is greater than or equal to zero.

(b) Find the time when the acceleration becomes zero.

(c) Find the velocity of the car when the acceleration is zero.

(d) How far does the car travel before the acceleration becomes zero?

3 A lift rises from ground level. The height, s metres, of the lift at time t seconds is given by $s = \frac{3t^2}{10} - \frac{t^3}{50}$ for $0 \leqslant t \leqslant 10$.

(a) Describe what happens to the lift when $t = 10$ s.

(b) Sketch a graph to show how the acceleration of the lift varies with time.

4 A car driver sees a red traffic light in front of him and starts to brake. The distance, s m, travelled while the car has been braking for t seconds is given by

$$s = \frac{45t}{2} - \frac{3t^2}{2} + \frac{t^3}{30}$$

This expression only applies while the car is moving.

(a) Find the range of values of t for which the expression for s is valid.

(b) Find the distance travelled while the car comes to rest.

(c) Sketch an acceleration–time graph for the car.

5 A firework manufacturer is designing a new type of firework. They want it to rise so that the height, h metres, at time t seconds is given by $h = 9t^2 - \dfrac{t^4}{12}$. The firework should explode when it reaches its maximum height.

Find the maximum height of the firework.

6 A weight is suspended from an elastic string. It moves up and down, so that at time t seconds the distance between the weight and the fixed end of the string is x metres, where $x = 0.8 + 0.4 \sin(0.5t)$.

(a) Find the velocity of the weight at time t.

(b) What is the maximum speed of the weight?

(c) Find the acceleration of the weight when $t = 2$.

(d) Find the range of values of the acceleration.

7 The height, h metres, of a hot air balloon at time t seconds is modelled by

$$h = 150\left(1 - \cos\left(\frac{t}{800}\right)\right)$$

The model is only valid while the balloon is gaining height.

(a) State the initial height of the balloon.

(b) Find the range of values of t for which the model is valid.

(c) What is the maximum height of the balloon?

(d) What is the maximum acceleration of the balloon?

8 A particle is set in motion with an initial speed of 20 m s^{-1} on a smooth horizontal surface. It slows down due to the action of air resistance, stopping after it has travelled 15 m. A possible model for the displacement, s m, at time t seconds is $s = A(1 - e^{-kt})$, where A and k are constants.

(a) State the value of A.

(b) Find k.

(c) Sketch a graph to show how the acceleration varies with time.

9 A particle, that hangs on a spring, moves so that the displacement, x metres, from its equilibrium position at time t seconds is given by $x = 4 \cos 2t + 3 \sin 2t$.

(a) Find the initial displacement of the particle.

(b) Find the initial speed of the particle.

(c) Show that the acceleration a m s^{-2}, satisfies the relationship $a = -4x$.

10 An object falls through a fluid so that the distance fallen, in metres, at time t seconds is given by $s = 40(4e^{-\frac{t}{4}} + t - 4)$.

  (a) Find the initial and terminal speeds of the object.

  (b) Sketch a graph to show how the acceleration of the object varies with time.

11 A particle is projected vertically, so that it moves under the influence of gravity and is subject to air resistance. The height, h metres, of the particle at time t seconds is given by

$$h = \frac{1}{k}\left(\frac{g}{k} + U\right)(1 - e^{-kt}) - \frac{gt}{k}$$

where k and U are constants. The model is only valid while the particle is moving upwards.

  (a) Show that the model is valid while

$$0 \leqslant t \leqslant \frac{1}{k}\ln\left(1 + \frac{kU}{g}\right).$$

  (b) Find the initial acceleration of the particle and sketch an acceleration–time graph for the particle.

12 A rocket that is launched at a firework display is to be modelled as a particle. The height, h metres, of the rocket at t seconds after lift-off is modelled by

$$h = \frac{5t^2}{2} - \frac{t^4}{20}.$$

The rocket rises vertically from rest and this model applies until the speed of the rocket drops to zero, when all the rocket's fuel has been used. The rocket then falls back to the ground.

  (a) Find expressions for the velocity and acceleration of the rocket as it rises.

  (b) Find the range of values of t for which the above model applies and the maximum height of the rocket in this period of time.

  (c) Describe what happens to the acceleration of the rocket while it is rising and find its maximum speed.

  (d) State **two** assumptions that it would be appropriate to make about the motion of the rocket after it has reached its maximum height, in order to predict the time it takes to fall back to the ground.   [A]

1.3 Acceleration to velocity and displacement

The process of differentiating to move from displacement to velocity and from velocity to acceleration can be reversed using integration.

> You can integrate an acceleration to obtain a velocity and integrate a velocity to obtain a displacement.
>
> $$v = \int a \, dt$$
>
> $$s = \int v \, dt$$

When using integration in this way it is very important to remember to include the constants of integration, which will depend on the initial velocities and positions of the objects that are under consideration.

The following examples illustrate the use of integration in this context.

Worked example 1.4

A car slows down from a speed of 30 m s^{-1}. Its acceleration, a m s^{-2} at time t seconds is given by $a = -\dfrac{t}{2}$. This expression is valid while the car is moving.

(a) Find an expression for the velocity of the car at time t.

(b) Find an expression for the distance travelled by the car at time t.

(c) Find the distance that the car travels before it stops.

Solution

(a) First integrate the acceleration to obtain the velocity, v m s^{-1}.

$$v = \int -\frac{t}{2} dt$$

$$= -\frac{t^2}{4} + c$$

The fact that the initial speed was 30 m s^{-1} can now be used to find c. Substituting $t = 0$ and $v = 30$ gives

$$30 = -\frac{0^2}{4} + c$$

$$c = 30$$

So the velocity at time t is

$$v = 30 - \frac{t^2}{4}$$

(b) The velocity can now be integrated to obtain the displacement, s metres.

$$s = \int 30 - \frac{t^2}{4} dt$$

$$= 30t - \frac{t^3}{12} + C$$

If we assume that the car starts at the origin, we can substitute $t = 0$ and $s = 0$, to determine the value of C.

$$0 = 30 \times 0 - \frac{0^3}{12} + C$$

$$C = 0$$

So the displacement at time t is given by

$$s = 30t - \frac{t^3}{12}$$

(c) The first step is to find t when the car stops.

$$0 = 30 - \frac{t^2}{4}$$

$$t^2 = 120$$

$$t = \sqrt{120}$$

This value for t can now be substituted into the expression obtained for the displacement.

$$s = 30 \times \sqrt{120} - \frac{(\sqrt{120})^3}{12}$$

$$= 219 \,\text{m (to 3 sf)}$$

Worked example 1.5

As a cyclist sets off from rest the acceleration, $a \,\text{m s}^{-2}$, of the cyclist, at time t seconds is given by $a = 1 - \frac{t}{20}$ for $0 \leqslant t \leqslant 20$.

(a) Find expressions for the velocity and displacement of the cyclist at time t.

(b) What is the speed of the cyclist after 20 seconds?

(c) How far does the cyclist travel in the 20 seconds?

Solution

(a) The acceleration should be integrated to give the velocity.

$$v = \int 1 - \frac{t}{20} dt$$

$$= t - \frac{t^2}{40} + c$$

As the cyclist starts at rest, substituting $t = 0$ and $v = 0$ will give c.

$$0 = 0 - \frac{0^2}{40} + c$$

$$c = 0$$

So the velocity at time t is given by $v = t - \frac{t^2}{40}$.

This can now be integrated to give the displacement.

$$s = \int t - \frac{t^2}{40} dt$$

$$= \frac{t^2}{2} - \frac{t^3}{120} + C$$

If we assume that the cyclist starts at the origin, then substituting $t = 0$ and $x = 0$ will give the value of C.

$$0 = \frac{0^2}{2} - \frac{0^3}{120} + C$$

$$C = 0$$

So the displacement at time t is given by $s = \frac{t^2}{2} - \frac{t^3}{120}$.

(b) We can now substitute $t = 20$ into the expression for the velocity.

$$v = 20 - \frac{20^2}{40}$$

$$= 10 \text{ m s}^{-1}$$

The cyclist reaches a speed of 10 m s^{-1}.

(c) Substituting $t = 20$ into the expression for s will give the distance travelled.

$$s = \frac{20^2}{2} - \frac{20^3}{120}$$

$$= 133\tfrac{1}{3} \text{ m}$$

Worked example 1.6

A parachutist is initially falling at a constant speed of 30 m s^{-1}, when he opens his parachute The acceleration, a m s^{-2}, of the parachutist t seconds after the parachute has been opened is modelled as $a = -13e^{-\frac{t}{2}}$.

(a) Find expressions for the velocity and the distance fallen by the parachutist at time t.

(b) Sketch a velocity–time graph for the parachutist.

(c) The parachutist must have a speed of less than 5 m s^{-1} when he lands. Find the minimum height at which he can open his parachute.

Solution

(a) First integrate the acceleration to find the velocity.

$$v = \int -13e^{-\frac{t}{2}}dt$$

$$= 26e^{-\frac{t}{2}} + c$$

Using the initial velocity, you can substitute $v = 30$ and $t = 0$ to find c.

$$30 = 26e^0 + c$$

$$c = 4$$

So the velocity at time t is given by $v = 26e^{-\frac{t}{2}} + 4$.

This can now be integrated to give the distance that has been fallen.

$$s = \int 26e^{-\frac{t}{2}} + 4dt$$

$$= -52e^{-\frac{t}{2}} + 4t + C$$

As the distance fallen will initially be zero you can substitute $t = 0$ and $s = 0$ to find C.

$$0 = -52e^0 + 4 \times 0 + C$$

$$C = 52$$

The distance fallen at time t is then

$$s = 52 - 52e^{-\frac{t}{2}} + 4t$$

$$= 52(1 - e^{-\frac{t}{2}}) + 4t$$

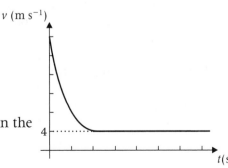

(b) The expression for the velocity shows that it decreases exponentially from 30 m s^{-1} to 4 m s^{-1}. This is shown in the graph.

(c) To find when the speed of the parachutist drops to 5 m s^{-1}, we must solve the equation below.

$$5 = 26e^{-\frac{t}{2}} + 4$$

$$e^{-\frac{t}{2}} = \frac{1}{26}$$

$$-\frac{t}{2} = \ln\left(\frac{1}{26}\right)$$

$$t = 2\ln(26)$$

$$= 6.52 \text{ s}$$

Now this value of t can be substituted into the expression for s.

$$s = 52\left(1 - e^{-\frac{2\ln 26}{2}}\right) + 4 \times 2\ln 26$$

$$= 76.1 \text{ m (to 3 sf)}$$

So the minimum safe height to open the parachute is 76.1 m.

EXERCISE 1B

1 The acceleration, $a \text{ m s}^{-2}$, at time t seconds of particle that starts at rest is given by $a = \dfrac{t^2}{100}$.

    (a) Find an expression for the velocity of the particle at time t.

    (b) Find the velocity of the particle when $t = 5$.

    (c) Find the distance that the particle travels in the first 5 seconds of its motion.

2 The acceleration of a cyclist, at time t seconds is given by $a = 2 - \dfrac{t}{10} \text{ m s}^{-2}$. This model is valid until $t = 20$ s. If the cyclist starts at rest, find the distance travelled in the 20 seconds and the final speed of the cyclist.

3 A body experiences an acceleration of $0.1t \text{ m s}^{-2}$, at time t seconds, for $0 \leqslant t \leqslant 5$. Its acceleration is zero for $t > 5$. Find the distance travelled by the body when $t = 10$, if it has an initial velocity of 3 m s^{-1}.

4 A train travels along a straight set of tracks. Initially it moves with velocity 10 m s^{-1}. It then experiences an acceleration given by $a = 0.1t(4 - t) \text{ m s}^{-2}$, until $t = 4$ s. Find the velocity when $t = 4$ and the distance travelled in this time.

5 The graph below shows how the magnitude of the force exerted on a lorry, of mass 10 000 kg, by its brakes varies with time. The lorry initially has a velocity of 20 m s^{-1}.

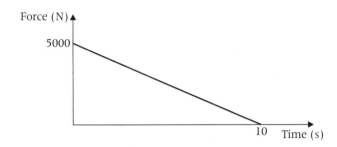

(a) Show that the acceleration, a m s^{-2}, at time t seconds is given by $a = \dfrac{t}{20} - \dfrac{1}{2}$ for $0 \leqslant t \leqslant 10$.

(b) Find the velocity of the lorry when $t = 10$.

(c) Find the distance travelled by the lorry in the 10 second period.

6 The acceleration of a car at time t seconds is $\dfrac{20 - t}{10}$ m s^{-2}.

The car starts at rest.

(a) Find an expression for the velocity of the car at time t.

(b) When is the acceleration of the car zero and what is its speed at this time ?

(c) The formula given above applies for $0 \leqslant t \leqslant 30$. Describe how the car moves during the 30 seconds.

(d) Find the total distance travelled by the car in the 30 second period.

7 A mass that is attached to one end of a spring moves up and down. The velocity, v m s^{-1}, at time t seconds of the mass is given by $v = 0.6 \sin 3t$.

(a) Find the acceleration of the mass at time t.

(b) Find the displacement of the mass at time t if its initial displacement is 0.8 m from the fixed end of the spring.

(c) Sketch a displacement–time graph for the mass.

8 The acceleration, a m s^{-2}, at time t seconds of a stone that falls from rest is modelled as $9.8e^{-2t}$.

(a) Find expressions for the velocity and displacement of the stone at time t.

(b) Sketch a velocity–time graph for the stone.

(c) How far would the stone fall in 20 seconds?

9 A bullet is fired vertically upwards, from ground level, with an initial velocity of 40 m s^{-1}. It's acceleration at time t seconds is modelled as $-50e^{-0.5t}$ m s^{-2}. This model only applies while the bullet is rising.

Find the maximum height of the bullet.

10 The tip of the blade in an electric jigsaw moves so that its acceleration is $40\cos(100\pi t)$ m s^{-2}, t seconds after it starts to move from rest at its lowest position.

  (a) Find the velocity of the tip of the blade at time t.

  (b) What is the maximum velocity of the tip of the blade?

  (c) What is the maximum displacement of the tip of the blade from its lowest position?

11 A particle moves so that its acceleration at time t seconds is $4 \sin 2t + 6 \cos 2t$ m s^{-2}. Initially the particle has a velocity of -2 m s^{-1} and is at the origin.

  (a) Find an expression for the position of the particle at time t.

  (b) Determine the maximum speed of the particle.

1.4 Motion in two or three dimensions

The ideas that you have used in one dimension can be very easily extended to two and three dimensions. A position vector would be written as $\mathbf{r} = x\mathbf{i} + x\mathbf{j} + z\mathbf{k}$ in three dimensions or as $\mathbf{r} = x\mathbf{i} + y\mathbf{j}$ in two dimensions. Here x, y and z are all functions of time. To obtain velocities and accelerations we simply need to differentiate these with respect to time. So in three dimensions we have

$$\mathbf{r} = x\mathbf{i} + y\mathbf{j} + z\mathbf{k}$$

$$\mathbf{v} = \frac{d\mathbf{r}}{dt}$$

$$= \frac{dx}{dt}\mathbf{i} + \frac{dy}{dt}\mathbf{j} + \frac{dz}{dt}\mathbf{k}$$

$$\mathbf{a} = \frac{d\mathbf{v}}{dt}$$

$$= \frac{d^2x}{dt^2}\mathbf{i} + \frac{d^2y}{dt^2}\mathbf{j} + \frac{d^2z}{dt^2}\mathbf{k}$$

In two dimensions these results reduce to

$$\mathbf{r} = x\mathbf{i} + y\mathbf{j}$$

$$\mathbf{v} = \frac{d\mathbf{r}}{dt}$$

$$= \frac{dx}{dt}\mathbf{i} + \frac{dy}{dt}\mathbf{j}$$

$$\mathbf{a} = \frac{d\mathbf{v}}{dt}$$

$$= \frac{d^2x}{dt^2}\mathbf{i} + \frac{d^2y}{dt^2}\mathbf{j}$$

These results are used in the following examples.

Worked example 1.7

The position vector, **r** m, at time t seconds of an aeroplane that is circling an airport is given by

$$\mathbf{r} = 500\sin\left(\frac{t}{20}\right)\mathbf{i} + 500\cos\left(\frac{t}{20}\right)\mathbf{j} + 4000\mathbf{k}$$

The unit vectors **i** and **j** are east and north, respectively, and **k** is vertical.

(a) Find the velocity of the aeroplane.

(b) Find the magnitude of the acceleration of the aeroplane.

Solution

(a) The velocity can be found by differentiating the position vector with respect to time.

$$\mathbf{v} = \frac{d\mathbf{r}}{dt}$$

$$= \frac{d}{dt}\left(500\sin\left(\frac{t}{20}\right)\right)\mathbf{i} + \frac{d}{dt}\left(500\cos\left(\frac{t}{20}\right)\right)\mathbf{j} + \frac{d}{dt}(4000)\mathbf{k}$$

$$= 25\cos\left(\frac{t}{20}\right)\mathbf{i} - 25\sin\left(\frac{t}{20}\right)\mathbf{j}$$

(b) The velocity can be differentiated to obtain the acceleration.

$$\mathbf{a} = \frac{d\mathbf{v}}{dt}$$

$$= \frac{d}{dt}\left(25\cos\left(\frac{t}{20}\right)\right)\mathbf{i} + \frac{d}{dt}\left(-25\sin\left(\frac{t}{20}\right)\right)\mathbf{j}$$

$$= -\frac{5}{4}\sin\left(\frac{t}{20}\right)\mathbf{i} - \frac{5}{4}\cos\left(\frac{t}{20}\right)\mathbf{j}$$

Now consider the magnitude of the acceleration.

$$a = \sqrt{\left(-\frac{5}{4}\sin\left(\frac{t}{20}\right)\right)^2 + \left(-\frac{5}{4}\cos\left(\frac{t}{20}\right)\right)^2}$$

$$= \frac{5}{4}\sqrt{\sin^2\left(\frac{t}{20}\right) + \cos^2\left(\frac{t}{20}\right)}$$

$$= \frac{5}{4}\ \text{m s}^{-2}$$

Obtaining a position vector

In the same way that accelerations and velocities were integrated in one dimension, you can integrate velocity or acceleration vectors to obtain velocities or displacements. In three dimensions we would integrate the acceleration to obtain the velocity.

$$\mathbf{a} = a_x\mathbf{i} + a_y\mathbf{j} + a_z\mathbf{k}$$

$$\mathbf{v} = \int \mathbf{a}dt$$

$$= \int a_x dt\mathbf{i} + \int a_y dt\mathbf{j} + \int a_z dt\mathbf{k}$$

Similarly we would integrate the velocity to get a position vector.

$$\mathbf{v} = v_x\mathbf{i} + v_y\mathbf{j} + v_z\mathbf{k}$$

$$\mathbf{r} = \int \mathbf{v}dt$$

$$= \int v_x dt\mathbf{i} + \int v_y dt\mathbf{j} + \int v_z dt\mathbf{k}$$

Note that when integrating like this you will introduce a number of constants of integration. It is important to determine each of these using the initial velocity and initial position or other similar information.

Worked example 1.8

A particle moves so that its acceleration, $\mathbf{a}$ m s^{-2}, at time t seconds is given by:

$$\mathbf{a} = 0.6t\mathbf{i} + (1 - 1.2t)\mathbf{j}$$

where $\mathbf{i}$ and $\mathbf{j}$ are perpendicular unit vectors.

(a) Find the velocity of the particle at time t if it has an initial velocity of $(2\mathbf{i} + 3\mathbf{j})$ m s^{-1}.

(b) Find an expression for the position of the particle at time t if its initial position is $20\mathbf{i}$ metres.

(c) Find the speed of the particle when $t = 2$.

Solution

(a) To find the velocity at time t integrate the acceleration vector:

$$\mathbf{v} = \int 0.6t dt\,\mathbf{i} + \int (1 - 1.2t)dt\,\mathbf{j}$$

$$= (0.3t^2 + c_1)\mathbf{i} + (t - 0.6t^2 + c_2)\mathbf{j}$$

Using the initial velocity, $2\mathbf{i} + 3\mathbf{j}$, gives $c_1 = 2$ and $c_2 = 3$, so that the velocity is:

$$\mathbf{v} = (0.3t^2 + 2)\mathbf{i} + (t - 0.6t^2 + 3)\mathbf{j}$$

(b) To find the position at time t integrate the velocity vector with respect to t:

$$\mathbf{r} = \int (0.3t^2 + 2)dt\,\mathbf{i} + \int (t - 0.6t^2 + 3)dt\,\mathbf{j}$$

$$= (0.1t^3 + 2t + c_3)\mathbf{i} + (0.5t^2 - 0.2t^3 + 3t + c_4)\mathbf{j}$$

Using the initial position of $20\mathbf{i}$ gives $c_3 = 20$ and $c_4 = 0$, so that the position is given by:

$$\mathbf{r} = (0.1t^3 + 2t + 20)\mathbf{i} + (0.5t^2 - 0.2t^3 + 3t)\mathbf{j}$$

(c) When $t = 2$:

$$\mathbf{v} = (0.3 \times 2^2 + 2)\mathbf{i} + (2 - 0.6 \times 2^2 + 3)\mathbf{j}$$

$$= 3.2\mathbf{i} + 2.6\mathbf{j}$$

Then the speed v is given by:

$$v = \sqrt{3.2^2 + 2.6^2}$$

$$= 4.12 \text{ m s}^{-1}$$

EXERCISE 1C

1   A particle moves so that, at time t seconds, its position vector in metres is given by:

$$\mathbf{r} = (t^2 - 5)\mathbf{i} + (4 - t + 6t^2)\mathbf{j}$$

(a)   Find the velocity and acceleration of the particle at time t.

(b)   Find the position and velocity of the particle when $t = 4$.

2   Two aeroplanes, A and B, move so that at time t seconds their position vectors, in metres, are given by

$$\mathbf{r}_A = (30t - 600)\mathbf{i} + (3t^2 - 120t + 1400)\mathbf{j}$$

and

$$\mathbf{r}_B = (20t + 10)\mathbf{i} + (40t - 10)\mathbf{j}$$

where $\mathbf{i}$ and $\mathbf{j}$ are unit vectors that are directed east and north, respectively.

(a)   Find the velocities of A and B at time t.

(b)   Find the speed of B.

(c)   Find the time when the two aeroplanes are travelling in parallel directions and the distance between them at this time.

3   A ball rolls on a slope so that its position is given by $\mathbf{r} = (t^2\mathbf{i} + 2t\mathbf{j})$ m at time t seconds, where $\mathbf{i}$ and $\mathbf{j}$ are perpendicular unit vectors. Find the velocity and acceleration the ball at time t.

4 A light aircraft moves so that its position, in metres, relative to an origin O, at time t seconds is given by

$$\mathbf{r} = \left(4t - \frac{t^2}{5}\right)\mathbf{i} + 10t\mathbf{j}$$

where $\mathbf{i}$ and $\mathbf{j}$ are unit vectors that are directed east and north, respectively.

(a) Find an expression for the velocity of the aircraft at time t.

(b) Find the time when the aircraft is due north of its initial position, and the distance from its initial position at that time.

(c) Find the time when the aircraft is travelling north and its speed at that time.

(d) Describe fully the acceleration of the aircraft.

5 The position, in metres, of a particle at time t seconds is given by:

$$\mathbf{r} = (t^2 - 8t + 2)\mathbf{i} + (2t^3 - 5t^2 + 6t)\mathbf{j}$$

where $\mathbf{i}$ and $\mathbf{j}$ are horizontal and vertical unit vectors, respectively. The mass of the particle is 3 kg.

(a) Find an expression for the velocity of the particle at time t.

(b) Find an expression for the resultant force acting on the particle at time t.

(c) Find when the horizontal component of the velocity is zero, and the position of the particle at this time.

6 The position, at time t seconds, of a car overtaking a lorry is modelled, in metres, as $\mathbf{r} = 20t\mathbf{i} + 5\left(t - \dfrac{t^2}{10}\right)\mathbf{j}$ where $\mathbf{i}$ and $\mathbf{j}$ are unit vectors parallel and perpendicular to the straight path of the lorry. The lorry travels along a straight line and has position, in metres, given by $\mathbf{r} = (10 + 15t)\mathbf{i}$ at time t seconds. Both the car and the lorry are modelled as particles.

(a) Find the time when the car is level with the lorry and its speed at this time.

(b) Find the time when the car is travelling parallel to the lorry and its acceleration at this time.

7 A force of magnitude $5t\mathbf{i} + 10t\mathbf{j}$ N acts on a body, of mass 50 kg, at time t seconds, for $0 \leqslant t \leqslant 5$. No force acts on the body for $t > 5$. Find the displacement of the body when $t = 10$, if it has an initial velocity of $3\mathbf{i}$ m s^{-1} and starts at the origin. The unit vectors $\mathbf{i}$ and $\mathbf{j}$ are perpendicular.

8 A particle moves so that its velocity, in m s^{-1}, at time t seconds is $\mathbf{v} = (4t^2 + 3)\mathbf{i} + (37.5 - 15t)\mathbf{j}$, where $\mathbf{i}$ and $\mathbf{j}$ are perpendicular unit vectors. Initially the particle is at the origin. When the particle is moving parallel to the unit vector $\mathbf{i}$ the magnitude of the resultant force acting on the particle is 80 N.

   (a) Find the mass of the particle.

   (b) Find the position of the particle when it is moving parallel to the unit vector $\mathbf{i}$.

9 A jet ski has an initial velocity of $(2\mathbf{i} + 5\mathbf{j})$ m s^{-1} and experiences an acceleration of $(\mathbf{i} + 0.2t\mathbf{j})$ m s^{-2}, at time t seconds. Find expressions for the velocity and position of the jet ski at time t seconds. Assume that the jet ski starts at the origin.

10 The acceleration of a particle at time t seconds is $(2t\mathbf{i} - 5t\mathbf{j})$ m s^{-2}. Initially the particle is at the origin and has velocity $(3\mathbf{i} + 6\mathbf{j})$ m s^{-1}.

   (a) Find an expression for the velocity of the particle at time t.

   (b) Find an expression for the position of the particle at time t.

11 The acceleration of a particle at time t seconds is $(4\mathbf{i} - t\mathbf{j})$ m s^{-2}. The particle is initially at rest at the point with position vector $(5\mathbf{i} - 10\mathbf{j})$ m. Note that $\mathbf{i}$ and $\mathbf{j}$ are perpendicular unit vectors.

   (a) Find an expression for the velocity of the particle at time t.

   (b) Find an expression for the position of the particle at time t.

12 An object that describes a circular path has a position vector, in metres, at time t seconds given by $\mathbf{r} = 4\sin(8t)\mathbf{i} + 4\cos(8t)\mathbf{j}$. Find the magnitude of the velocity and acceleration of the object.

13 A particle follows a path so that its position at time t is given by

$$\mathbf{r} = 4\cos(2t)\mathbf{i} + 3\sin(2t)\mathbf{j}.$$

   (a) Find the position, velocity and acceleration of the particle when $t = \dfrac{\pi}{2}$.

   (b) Show that the magnitude of the acceleration at time t is

$$\sqrt{(144 + 112\cos^2(2t))}$$

   and find its maximum and minimum values.   [A]

14 The position vector of smoke particles as they leave a chimney for the first 4 s of their motion is given by

$$\mathbf{r} = 4t\mathbf{i} + \left(\frac{3t^2}{2}\right)\mathbf{j} + 6t\mathbf{k},$$

where **i** and **k** are horizontal, directed north and east, respectively, and **j** is vertically upward.

(a) What is the magnitude and direction of the acceleration of the smoke?

(b) What is
   (i) the velocity, and
   (ii) the speed
   of the smoke particles after 2 s?

(c) Calculate the angle between the direction of the smoke and the ground when $t = 2$.

15 A glider spirals upwards in a thermal (hot air current) so that its position vector with respect to a point on the ground is

$$\mathbf{r} = \left(100 \cos \frac{t}{5}\right)\mathbf{i} + \left(200 + \frac{t}{3}\right)\mathbf{j} + \left(100 \sin \frac{t}{5}\right)\mathbf{k}.$$

The directions of **i**, **j** and **k** are as defined in Question **14**.

(a) Determine the glider's speed at $t = 0$, 5π and 10π seconds. What do you notice?

(b) Find **r** when $t = 0$ and 10π seconds and find the height risen in one complete turn of the spiral.

16 A particle moves in a horizontal plane and its position vector at time t is relative to a fixed origin O is given by

$$\mathbf{r} = (2 \sin t\mathbf{i} + \cos t\mathbf{j}) \text{ m}.$$

Find the values of t in the range $0 \leqslant t \leqslant \pi$ when the speed of the particle is a maximum. [A]

17 The diagram shows the path of a car that overtakes a lorry on a straight road.

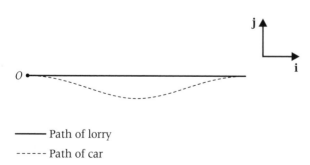

———— Path of lorry

------ Path of car

Two alternative models for the position of the car during the 10 seconds that it takes to pass the lorry are:

Model A $\qquad \mathbf{r} = 20t\mathbf{i} - 1.6\left(t - \dfrac{t^2}{10}\right)\mathbf{j};$

Model B $\qquad \mathbf{r} = 20t\mathbf{i} - 2\left(1 - \cos\dfrac{\pi t}{5}\right)\mathbf{j}.$

(a) For each model find the position and velocity of the car when $t = 0$, 5 and 10.

(b) Which is the better model for the motion of the car? Briefly state your main reason. [A]

18 A possible model for the position of a car, at time t seconds, while it is travelling over a small hill is:

$$\mathbf{r} = 25t\mathbf{i} + \frac{50}{\pi}\left(1 - \cos\left(\frac{\pi t}{10}\right)\right)\mathbf{j}$$

where $\mathbf{i}$ and $\mathbf{j}$ are horizontal and vertical unit vectors, respectively, and the distances are in metres. The model is valid for $0 \leqslant t \leqslant 20$. The diagram shows the path of the car. Initially the car is at O, time $t = 0$.

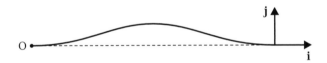

(a) Find the velocity of the car at time t.

(b) Find an expression for the speed of the car, at time t.

(c) Find the times when the car has its minimum and maximum speeds and describe what happens to the speed of the car as it travels over the hill.

(d) Comment on how your answer to part (**c**) agrees or disagrees with the way that you would expect the speed of a car to change while going over a hill. [A]

Key point summary

I In one, two or three dimensions displacements or position vectors can be differentiated to give velocities and accelerations.   *p2*

2 Accelerations can be integrated to give velocities and position vectors or displacements.   *p2*

Formulae to learn

$$v = \frac{dx}{dt}$$

$$a = \frac{dv}{dt}$$

$$a = \frac{d^2x}{dt^2}$$

$$v = \int a\, dt$$

$$s = \int v\, dt$$

$$\mathbf{r} = x\mathbf{i} + y\mathbf{j} + z\mathbf{k}$$

$$\mathbf{v} = \frac{d\mathbf{r}}{dt}$$

$$= \frac{dx}{dt}\mathbf{i} + \frac{dy}{dt}\mathbf{j} + \frac{dz}{dt}\mathbf{k}$$

$$\mathbf{a} = \frac{d\mathbf{v}}{dt}$$

$$= \frac{d^2x}{dt^2}\mathbf{i} + \frac{d^2y}{dt^2}\mathbf{j} + \frac{d^2z}{dt^2}\mathbf{k}$$

$$\mathbf{v} = \int \mathbf{a}\, dt$$

$$\mathbf{r} = \int \mathbf{v}\, dt$$

Test yourself	**What to review**

1 The displacement, s metres, of a particle at time t seconds is given by $s = 5t + 6e^{-2t} - 4$.

   (a) Find the initial velocity of the particle.

   (b) Sketch a velocity–time graph for the particle.

   (c) Find the acceleration at time t seconds.

Section 1.2

2 A particle moves so that at time t seconds its acceleration is $-\left(\dfrac{\sqrt{t}}{4}\right)$ m s^{-2}. Its initial velocity is 16 m s^{-1}, when it passes the origin.

Find the displacement of the particle from the origin when it comes to rest.

Section 1.3

3 A particle, of mass 5 kg, moves so that its position vector at time t is given by:

$$\mathbf{r} = (6 + 2t)\mathbf{i} + (8 - 3t^2)\mathbf{j}$$

where $\mathbf{i}$ and $\mathbf{j}$ are perpendicular unit vectors.

   (a) Find the position of the particle when $t = 10$.

   (b) Find the velocity of the particle in terms of t.

   (c) Find the speed of the particle when $t = 2$.

   (d) Find the acceleration of the particle in terms of t.

Section 1.4

4 A particle moves so that its acceleration, $\mathbf{a}$ m s^{-2}, at time t seconds is given by

$$\mathbf{a} = 0.6t\mathbf{i} + (1 - 1.2t)\mathbf{j}$$

where $\mathbf{i}$ and $\mathbf{j}$ are perpendicular unit vectors.

   (a) Find the velocity of the particle at time t if it has an initial velocity of $(2\mathbf{i} + 3\mathbf{j})$ m s^{-1}.

   (b) Find an expression for the position of the particle at time t if its initial position is $20\mathbf{i}$.

   (c) Find the speed of the particle when $t = 2$.

Section 1.4

Test yourself **ANSWERS**

1 (a) -7 m s^{-1} **(c)** $a = 24e^{-2t}$.

2 201 m.

3 (a) $26\mathbf{i} - 292\mathbf{j}$, **(b)** $2\mathbf{i} - 6t\mathbf{j}$, **(c)** 12.2, **(d)** $-6\mathbf{j}$.

4 (a) $\mathbf{v} = (2 + 0.3t^2)\mathbf{i} + (3 + t - 0.6t^2)\mathbf{j}$,

  (b) $\mathbf{r} = (20 + 2t + 0.1t^3)\mathbf{i} + (3t + 0.5t^2 - 0.2t^3)\mathbf{j}$.

  (c) 4.12 m s^{-1}.

CHAPTER 2

Energy

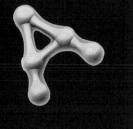

Learning objectives

After studying this chapter you should be able to:

- calculate kinetic energy
- calculate work done by a constant force
- calculate gravitational potential energy
- calculate elastic potential energy
- be able to use power.

2.1 Kinetic energy

Every moving body has kinetic energy. The greater the mass and the greater the speed, the greater the kinetic energy.

> The kinetic energy of a body is defined as $\frac{1}{2}mv^2$, where m is the mass of the body and v its speed.

The units of energy are joules (J).

Worked example 2.1

A car has mass 1100 kg. At the bottom of a hill it is travelling at 30 m s^{-1} and loses speed as it travels up the hill. At the top of the hill its speed is 22 m s^{-1}. Calculate the amount of kinetic energy lost as the car drove up the hill.

Solution

At the bottom of the hill;

$$\text{Kinetic energy} = \frac{1}{2} \times 1100 \times 30^2$$
$$= 495\,000 \text{ J}$$

At the top of the hill;

$$\text{Kinetic energy} = \frac{1}{2} \times 1100 \times 22^2$$
$$= 266\,200 \text{ J}$$

Now the amount of kinetic energy that has been lost can be calculated.

$$\text{Kinetic energy lost} = 495\,000 - 266\,200$$
$$= 228\,800 \text{ J}$$

2

EXERCISE 2A

1 Calculate the kinetic energy of a ball, of mass 150 grams, travelling at 8 m s^{-1}.

2 Calculate the kinetic energy of a train, of mass 30 000 tonnes, travelling at 50 m s^{-1}.

3 A ball has a mass of 200 grams. It is thrown so that its initial speed is 12 m s^{-1} and during its flight it has a minimum speed of 6 m s^{-1}. Calculate the minimum and maximum values of the kinetic energy of the ball.

4 A light aeroplane has a mass of 1500 kg. When it lands it is travelling at 80 m s^{-1} and at the end of the runway its speed has been reduced to 10 m s^{-1}. Calculate how much kinetic energy has been lost.

5 A stone, of mass 50 grams, is dropped from the top of a cliff at a height of 40 m.

   (a) Assume that no resistance forces act on the stone and calculate its speed at the bottom of the cliff.

   (b) How much kinetic energy does the stone gain as it falls.

6 A cycle and cyclist have mass 70 kg. The cyclist freewheels from rest down a slope, accelerating at 0.5 ms^{-2}. The initial speed of the cyclist is 3 m s^{-1}.

   (a) Calculate the speed of the cyclist after he has travelled 50 m.

   (b) Calculate the increase in the kinetic energy of the cyclist.

2.2 Work and energy

As a stone falls its kinetic energy increases. As you start to pedal a cycle your kinetic energy increases. In the first of these cases gravity is the force that causes a change in kinetic energy. In the second the cyclist exerts a force. In this section you will examine the relationship between the change in the kinetic energy of a body and the forces that act on it.

If a constant force of magnitude F acts on a body of mass m, it will produce an acceleration of $\dfrac{F}{m}$, this can be substituted into the constant acceleration equation $v^2 = u^2 + 2as$, to give

$$v^2 = u^2 + 2 \times \frac{F}{m} \times s$$

or

$$\tfrac{1}{2}mv^2 - \tfrac{1}{2}mu^2 = Fs$$

This equation can be expressed as

    Change in kinetic energy $= Fs$

> The quantity *Fs* is referred to as the work done by the force. It is this work that determines the change in the kinetic energy of the body that the force causes.

Worked example 2.2

A ball, of mass 0.4 kg, is released from rest and allowed to fall 3 m.

(a) Find the work done by gravity as the ball falls.

(b) State the gain in kinetic energy of the ball.

(c) Calculate the speed of the ball when it has fallen 3 m.

Solution

(a) The work done is calculated using *Fs*. In this case

$$F = mg$$
$$= 0.4 \times 9.8$$
$$= 3.92 \text{ N}$$

The work done by gravity can be calculated.

$$\text{Work done} = Fs$$
$$= 3.92 \times 3$$
$$= 11.76 \text{ J}$$

(b) As the gain in kinetic energy is equal to the work done, there is a gain in kinetic energy of 11.76 J.

(c) The kinetic energy of the ball is 11.76 J, so the speed can be calculated as below;

$$11.76 = \tfrac{1}{2} \times 0.4 \, v^2$$
$$v^2 = 58.8$$
$$v = \sqrt{58.8}$$
$$= 7.67 \text{ m s}^{-1} \text{ (to 3 sf)}$$

Worked example 2.3

A box is initially at rest on a smooth horizontal surface. The mass of the box is 5 kg. A horizontal force of magnitude 8 N acts on the box as it slides 6 m.

(a) Find the work done by the force.

(b) Find the speed of the box when it has travelled 6 m.

Solution

(a) The work done is calculated using *Fs*.

$$\text{Work done} = 8 \times 6$$
$$= 48\,\text{J}$$

(b) Using the fact that the work done is equal to the change in kinetic energy gives

$$48 = \tfrac{1}{2} \times 5v^2$$
$$v = \sqrt{19.2}$$
$$= 4.38\,\text{m s}^{-1}\ (\text{to 3 sf})$$

In most situations more than one force will act. Some forces may act in the direction of motion, as in the previous examples, but often they will act in the opposite direction to the motion. These types of forces will include resistance and friction forces. A force that acts in the opposite direction to the motion will do a negative amount of work. For example the work done by a friction force of magnitude 80 N acting on a body that moves 5 m would be −400 J. Often we would say that the work done against friction is 400 J.

Worked example 2.4

A car, of mass 1250 kg, is subject to a forward force of magnitude 2000 N and a resistance force of magnitude 500 N. The car moves 200 m.

(a) Find the work done by each of the forces acting on the car.

(b) If the car is initially moving at 5 m s⁻¹, find the final speed of the car.

Solution

(a) The work done by the 2000 N force is $2000 \times 200 = 400\,000\,\text{J}$.

The work done by the 500 N force is $-500 \times 200 = -100\,000\,\text{J}$. We might say that the work done against friction is 100 000 J. Total work done $= 400\,000 - 100\,000 = 300\,000\,\text{J}$

Alternatively note that the resultant is 1500 N and the work done will be $1500 \times 200 = 300\,000\,\text{J}$.

(b) The change in kinetic energy is 300 000 J. So the final speed can be calculated

$$300\,000 = \tfrac{1}{2} \times 1250 \times v^2 - \tfrac{1}{2} \times 1250 \times 5^2$$
$$v^2 = 505$$
$$v = \sqrt{505}$$
$$= 22.5\,\text{m s}^{-1}\ (\text{to 3 sf})$$

Worked example 2.5

A ball, of mass 0.3 kg, is moving at 8 m s^{-1} when it enters a tank of water. It hits the bottom of the tank travelling at 2 m s^{-1}. The depth of water in the tank is 1.2 m. Assume that a constant resistance force acts on the ball as it moves through the water.

(a) Calculate the change in the kinetic energy of the ball.

(b) Find the magnitude of the resistance force that acts on the ball.

Solution

(a) Change in kinetic energy $= \frac{1}{2} \times 0.3 \times 2^2 - \frac{1}{2} \times 0.3 \times 8^2$
$$= -9 \text{ J}$$

(b) First consider the work done by each of the forces.

Work done by gravity $= 0.3 \times 9.8 \times 1.2$
$$= 3.528 \text{ J}$$

If the resistance force has magnitude R, then the work done by this force will be

$$-R \times 1.2 = -1.2R$$

and so the total work done is

$$3.528 - 1.2R.$$

Now we can find R by using

Change in kinetic energy $=$ work done
$$-9 = 3.528 - 1.2R$$
$$R = \frac{3.528 + 9}{1.2}$$
$$= 10.44 \text{ N}$$

EXERCISE 2B

1 A force of magnitude 800 N acts on a car, of mass 1000 kg, as it moves 400 m on a horizontal surface. Assume that no other forces act on the car.

(a) Calculate the work done by the force that acts on the car.

(b) Find the final kinetic energy and speed of the car if it is initially

   (i) at rest,

   (ii) moving at 3 m s^{-1}.

2 A force acts horizontally on a package, of mass 4 kg, that is initially at rest on a smooth horizontal surface. After the package has moved 3 m its speed is 5 m s^{-1}.

(a) Find the increase in the kinetic energy of the package.

(b) How much work is done by the force that acts on the package?

(c) Determine the magnitude of the force that acts on the package.

3 A brick, of mass 2 kg, is allowed to fall from rest at a height of 3.2 m. Find the kinetic energy and speed of the brick when it hits the ground;

(a) assuming that no resistance forces act on the brick as it falls,

(b) assuming that a constant resistance force of magnitude 10 N acts on the brick.

4 A rope is attached to a boat, of mass 200 kg. The boat is pulled along a horizontal surface by the horizontal rope. The tension in the rope remains constant at 500 N. When the boat has moved 50 m its speed is 0.4 m s^{-1}.

(a) Calculate the work done by the tension in the rope.

(b) Calculate the final kinetic energy of the boat.

(c) Find the work done against the resistance forces acting on the boat.

(d) Find the magnitude of the resistance force if it is assumed to be constant.

5 A ball of mass 200 grams is dropped from a height of 1 m. The ball is initially at rest. It hits the ground and rebounds at $\frac{3}{4}$ of the speed with which it hit the ground. Find the energy lost by the ball as it bounces and the height to which it rebounds.

6 A forward force of magnitude 2500 N acts on a car, of mass 1250 kg, as it moves 500 m. The initial speed of the car was 12 m s^{-1}. All the motion takes place along a straight line.

(a) If no resistance forces act on the car find its final kinetic energy and speed.

(b) If the final speed of the car is 30 m s^{-1}, find the work done against the resistance forces and the average magnitude of the resistance force.

7 As a car, of mass 1200 kg, skids 25 m, on a horizontal surface, its speed is reduced from 30 m s^{-1} to 20 m s^{-1}.

   (a) Find the energy lost by the car as it skids.

   (b) If the coefficient of friction between the car and the road is 0.8, find the work done by the friction force.

   (c) Find the work done by the air resistance force that acts on the car.

   (d) Assuming that the air resistance force is constant, find out how much further the car travels before it stops.

   (e) Criticise the assumptions that you have used to get your answer to part **(d)** and suggest how using a more realistic model would change your answer.

8 A diver, of mass 60 kg, dives from a diving board at a height of 4 m. She hits the water travelling at a speed of 8 m s^{-1} and descends to a depth of 2 m in the diving pool. Model the diver as a particle.

   (a) Find the work done against air resistance before the diver hits the water and the average magnitude of the air resistance force.

   (b) Find the average magnitude of the force exerted by the water on the diver as she is brought to rest in the diving pool.

9 A ball of mass 500 grams is dropped from a height of 3 m. It hits the ground and travels down 6 cm into soft mud before stopping. Assume no air resistance acts on the ball as it falls.

   (a) Find the average force that the mud exerts on the ball while it is slowing down.

   (b) A different ball of mass 200 grams hits the mud travelling at 6 m s^{-1}. Assume that the mud exerts the same force on the ball and find the distance that it travels into the mud before stopping.

10 A bullet fired into an earth bank at an unknown speed penetrates to a distance of 2 m. An identical bullet fired at a speed of 120 m s^{-1} travels 3 m into the bank. If the mass of this type of bullet is 20 grams, find the average force exerted on the bullets by the earth, and the speed at which the first bullet was fired.

2.3 Forces at angles

If a force acts at an angle to the direction of motion to the body that it acts on, then we must use the component of the force in the direction of motion when calculating the work done.

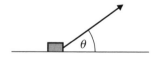

If the force shown in the diagram acts as the body moves a distance d, then the work done is $Fd \cos \theta$.

Worked example 2.6

A force, of magnitude 60 N, acts at an angle of 30° above the horizontal on a sack, of mass 50 kg, that is initially at rest on a horizontal surface. Find the work done by the force and the final speed of the sack which moves 5 m and;

(a) the surface is smooth

(b) the coefficient of friction between the sack and the surface is 0.1.

Solution

(a) The work done can be calculated using $Fd \cos \theta$.

$$\text{Work done} = 60 \times 5 \times \cos 30°$$
$$= 300 \times \frac{\sqrt{3}}{2}$$
$$= 150\sqrt{3} \text{ J}$$

The work done is equal to the gain in kinetic energy, so

$$150\sqrt{3} \text{ J} = \tfrac{1}{2} \times 50v^2$$
$$v^2 = 6\sqrt{3}$$
$$v = 3.22 \text{ m s}^{-1} \text{ (to 3 sf)}$$

(b) The work done by the force will be the same, but the final kinetic energy will be less due to the friction force. First we must calculate the magnitude of the friction force.

Resolving vertically to find the normal reaction, R, we have

$$R + 60 \sin 30° = 50 \times 9.8$$
$$R = 460 \text{ N}$$

Then the magnitude of the friction force can now be found using $F = \mu R$, which in this case gives

$$F = 0.1 \times 460$$
$$= 46 \text{ N}$$

The work done by the friction force will be

$$-46 \times 5 = -230 \text{ J}$$

The total work done is then $150\sqrt{3} - 230$.
The speed can now be found using work done equals change in kinetic energy.

$$150\sqrt{3} - 230 = \tfrac{1}{2} \times 50v^2$$
$$v = 1.09 \text{ m s}^{-1} \text{ (to 3 sf)}$$

Worked example 2.7

A particle, of mass 5 kg, is initially at rest. It slides 4 m down a slope at 30°. Assume that the slope is smooth and that there is no air resistance.

(a) Find the work done by gravity as the particle slides down the slope.

(b) Find the speed of the particle, when it has travelled the 4 m.

Solution

(a) The work done can be calculated using $Fd \cos \theta$.

$$\text{Work done} = 5 \times 9.8 \times 4 \cos 60°$$
$$= 98 \text{ J}$$

(b) Using work done equals change in kinetic energy gives

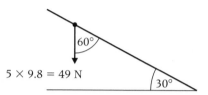

$$98 = \tfrac{1}{2} \times 5v^2$$
$$v = \sqrt{39.2}$$
$$= 6.26 \text{ m s}^{-1} \text{ (to 3 sf)}$$

Gravitational potential energy

Consider a particle of mass m that falls vertically a distance h, in the absence of any resistance forces. The work done by gravity will be given by mgh.

Also consider a second particle of the same mass that slides down the smooth slope shown in the diagram.

The particle will slide a distance of $\dfrac{h}{\sin \theta}$.

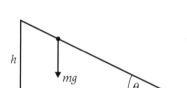

So the work done by gravity is

$$mg \times \frac{h}{\sin \theta} \times \cos (90 - \theta) = mg \times \frac{h}{\sin \theta} \times \sin \theta = mgh$$

Note that in both of these examples the work done by gravity is the same and depends on the initial height and not the route taken. A curved surface would have also produced the same result. The important feature of this result is that there are no resistance or friction forces present.

This quantity mgh is often referred to as the gravitational potential energy of the body and often this is abbreviated to potential energy or PE. If a body is allowed to fall, swing or slide the potential energy will be converted to kinetic energy. Similarly as a body rises its kinetic energy will be converted to potential energy. This gives a useful way of approaching some problems, because the total energy will remain constant if no resistance or friction forces act.

Gravitational potential energy $= mgh$

Worked example 2.8

A soldier, of mass 72 kg, on a training exercise is running at a speed of 5 m s^{-1}. He grabs hold of a rope, of length 6 m, that is hanging vertically. He then swings on the rope.

(a) Calculate the initial kinetic energy of the soldier.

(b) Calculate the speed of the soldier when he has risen 0.5 m.

(c) Find the maximum height of the soldier and the angle between the rope and the vertical at this time.

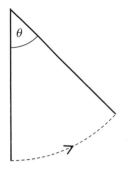

2

Solution

(a) The initial kinetic energy can be calculated from the information given

$$KE = \tfrac{1}{2} \times 72 \times 5^2$$
$$= 900 \text{ J}$$

(b) When the soldier has risen 0.5 m his potential energy can be calculated

$$PE = 72 \times 9.8 \times 0.5$$
$$= 352.8 \text{ J}$$

The remaining kinetic energy can then be calculated as

$$900 - 352.8 = 547.2$$

The speed of the soldier can now be found

$$547.2 = \tfrac{1}{2} \times 72v^2$$
$$v = \sqrt{15.2}$$
$$= 3.90 \text{ m s}^{-1} \text{ (to 3 sf)}$$

(c) At the soldier's highest point, all his initial kinetic energy will have been converted to potential energy. This gives the equation

$$72 \times 9.8h = 900$$
$$h = 1.28 \text{ m (to 3 sf)}$$

By considering the triangle in the diagram

$$\cos \theta = \frac{6 - 1.28}{6}$$

$$\theta = 38° \text{ to the nearest degree.}$$

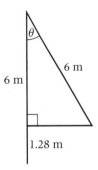

Worked example 2.9

A cyclist and cycle of combined mass 80 kg freewheel down a slope. They travel a distance of 100 m down the slope which is at an angle α to the horizontal, where $\sin \alpha = \frac{1}{10}$. The speed of the cyclist increases from 4 m s^{-1} to 8 m s^{-1}.

(a) Find the change in the total energy of the cycle and cyclist at the top and bottom of the slope.

(b) Find the work done against resistance forces while the cyclist travelled down the slope and the magnitude of the average resistance force on the cyclist.

(c) Find the speed of the cyclist when he has travelled 20 m down the slope.

Solution

(a) We must consider the gain in kinetic energy and the potential energy that is lost.

$$\text{Gain in KE} = \tfrac{1}{2} \times 80 \times 8^2 - \tfrac{1}{2} \times 80 \times 4^2$$
$$= 1920 \, \text{J}$$

$$\text{Loss of PE} = 80 \times 9.8 \times 100 \sin \alpha$$
$$= 80 \times 9.8 \times 100 \times \tfrac{1}{10}$$
$$= 7840 \, \text{J}$$

$$\text{Change in energy} = 1920 - 7840$$
$$= -5920 \, \text{J}$$

So 5920 J of energy has been lost.

(b) The energy has been lost due to the work done against friction, so

$$\text{Work done against resistance forces} = 5920 \, \text{J}$$

The average resistance force can be found by dividing the work done by the distance travelled.

$$\text{Average resistance force} = \frac{5920}{100} = 59.2 \, \text{N}$$

(c) As the cycle and cyclist travel the 20 m, the resistance force will act. So first calculate the work done against these forces.

$$\text{Work done against resistance forces} = 20 \times 59.2 = 1184 \, \text{J}$$

As the cycle and cyclist travel down the slope more potential energy is lost.

$$\text{Loss of PE} = 80 \times 9.8 \times 20 \times \tfrac{1}{10} = 1568 \, \text{J}$$

The gain in kinetic energy will then be $1568 - 1184 = 384$ J. The initial KE is given by

$$\tfrac{1}{2} \times 80 \times 4^2 = 640 \, \text{J}$$

The final kinetic energy will then be $640 + 384 = 1024$ J. Now the final speed can be found

$$\tfrac{1}{2} \times 80v^2 = 1024 \, \text{J}$$
$$v = \sqrt{25.6}$$
$$= 5.06 \, \text{m s}^{-1} \text{ (to 3 sf)}$$

EXERCISE 2C

1 The diagram shows a curved slide with a drop of 5 m. A child, of mass 50 kg, sits at the top of the slide. He slides down. Assume that there are no resistance or friction forces acting on the slide. Calculate:

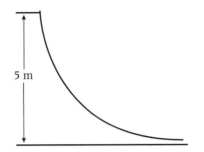

(a) the potential energy that the child would lose as he slides from the top to the bottom of the slide,

(b) the speed of the child at the bottom of the slide.

2 A stone, of mass 0.8 kg, is thrown over a cliff at speed of 3 m s^{-1}. It hits the water at a speed of 12 m s^{-1}.

(a) Find the potential energy lost by the stone.

(b) Find the height of the cliff.

3 A particle, of mass 3 kg, slides down a slope of length 20 m, which is inclined at an angle of 45° to the horizontal. At the top of the slope the particle has an initial speed of 4 m s^{-1}. Assume that the slope is smooth.

(a) Find the potential lost energy lost by the particle as slides down the slope.

(b) Find the kinetic energy and the speed of the particle at the bottom of the slope.

(c) If a constant friction force of magnitude 5 N acts on the particle as it slides, find the speed of the particle at the bottom of the slope.

4 A child, of mass 60 kg, swings on a rope of length 8 m. The rope is initially at an angle of 30° to the vertical. The child initially moves at 2 m s^{-1}.

(a) Find the potential energy that is lost as the child swings to her lowest point.

(b) Find the maximum kinetic energy and the maximum speed of the child.

(c) Find the maximum height of the child above her lowest position.

5 A ball of mass 300 grams is kicked so that it has an initial speed of 12 m s^{-1}. During its flight the speed of the ball has a minimum value of 4 m s^{-1}.

(a) Find the initial kinetic energy of the ball.

(b) Find the maximum potential energy of the ball.

(c) Find the maximum height of the ball.

6 A loop-the-loop roller coaster is shown in the diagram. At point A at the top of the first loop the roller coaster is moving at 8 m s⁻¹. The mass of the roller coaster carriage is 400 kg. Assume that no resistance forces act on the roller coaster. The diameter of the first loop is 5 m and the diameter of the second loop is 3 m.

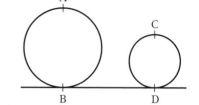

(a) Find the kinetic energy of the carriage at the bottom of the first loop.

(b) Find the kinetic energy of the carriage at the top of the second loop.

(c) Find the maximum speed of the roller coaster.

7 A sledge, of mass 12 kg, is pulled by a rope that is at an angle of 20° to the horizontal. The tension in the rope is a constant 80 N. The coefficient of friction between the sledge and the horizontal ground on which it moves is 0.2. Find the kinetic energy and the speed of the sledge when it has moved 5 m from rest.

8 A roller coaster, of mass 500 kg, is at the top of a slope and travelling at 4 m s⁻¹. As it travels down the slope its speed increases to 10 m s⁻¹. The length of the slope is 20 m and the top is 12 m higher than the bottom. At the bottom of the slope it travels on a horizontal section of track. Model the roller coaster as a particle that has a constant resistance force acting on it.

(a) Find the energy lost by the roller coaster as it moves down the slope.

(b) Find the magnitude of the resistance force on the roller coaster.

(c) Find how far the roller coaster travels along the horizontal section of the track before it comes to rest.

9 A car, of mass 1100 kg, is travelling down a hill, inclined at an angle of 5° to the horizontal. The driver brakes hard and skids 15 m. The coefficient of friction between the tyres and the road is 0.7. Find the initial kinetic energy and speed of the car.

10 The diagram shows a slide that is in the shape of a semicircle of radius 5 m and that has centre O. The users slide down the inside of the slide and up the other side. They all start at rest at the top of the slide, at the point A. The mass of a user is 55 kg.

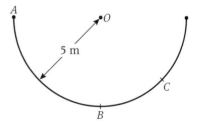

(a) If the slide is smooth find the maximum kinetic energy of a user and their maximum speed.

In fact the slide is not smooth. A simple model assumes that a constant resistance force acts on the users and the magnitude of this is 30 N.

(b) Calculate the speed of a user at the lowest point of the slide, marked B on the diagram.

(c) A person using the slide comes to rest at the point marked C. Find the angle BOC. (Hint: use a numerical method to solve your equation.)

11 A soldier, of mass 80 kg, swings on a rope of length 80 m. He is to be modelled as a particle that describes a circular arc from *A*, through *B* to *C*. The path is shown in the following diagram.

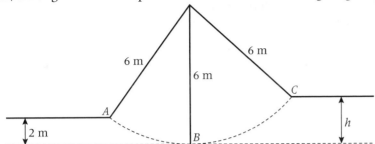

The point *A* is 2 m higher than *B* and *C* is *h* m higher than *B*. Initially the soldier moves at 2 m s^{-1} at *A* and in a direction perpendicular to the rope.

(a) Find the kinetic energy of the soldier at *B*, stating any assumptions that you make.

(b) Find *h*, if the soldier comes to rest at *C* before swinging back.

(c) Explain why the tension does no work in this situation. [A]

12 The diagram shows part of the track of a roller coaster ride, which has been modelled as a number of straight lengths of track. The roller coaster's carriages are modelled as a particle of mass 400 kg, which can negotiate the bends *A*, *B*, *C* and *D* without any loss of speed. The speed of the roller coaster at *A* is 3 m s^{-1} and at *B* it is 10 m s^{-1}.

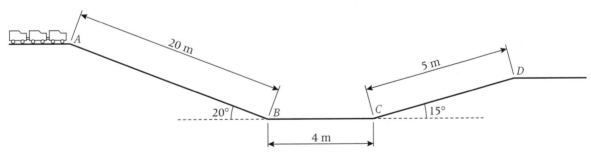

(a) Show that the work done against the resistance forces, as the roller coaster moves from *A* to *B*, is approximately 8610 J and use this to find the magnitude of the resistance forces, assuming that they are constant.

(b) Using the magnitude of the resistance forces found in **(a)**, show that the speed of the roller coaster at *D* is approximately 7.4 m s^{-1} and find how far along the horizontal track beyond *D* it could travel before stopping.

(c) Describe **two** ways in which this model could be improved. [A]

2.4 Hooke's law

This section will consider the work done by variable forces, but will first introduce Hooke's law, which predicts the tension in a string or spring. Hooke's law will be used extensively in the later sections of this chapter.

Hooke's law provides a simple but effective model for the tension in a spring.

> Hooke's law simply states that the tension T is given by
>
> $$T = \frac{\lambda x}{l}$$
>
> where λ is a constant called the modulus of elasticity, l is the natural or unstretched length of the spring and x is the extension of the spring. The modulus of elasticity depends on the material that the spring is made from and the way in which it has been constructed.

Note that when working with Hooke's law all lengths should be in metres and that the units of λ are newtons.

If a spring is compressed instead of stretched, then Hooke's law can be used to calculate the thrust exerted by the spring.

Hooke's law can also be applied to elastic strings.

Worked example 2.10

A particle, of mass 5 kg, is suspended from a spring, of natural length 0.2 m and modulus of elasticity 40 N. Find the extension of the spring when the particle is in equilibrium.

Solution

The diagram shows the forces acting on the particle. In equilibrium, the upward tension will balance the weight of the particle. This gives

$$T = 5 \times 9.8$$
$$= 49 \text{ N}$$

Using Hooke's law this becomes;

$$\frac{40x}{0.2} = 49$$
$$x = 0.245 \text{ m}$$

Worked example 2.11

A spring has natural length 0.5 m. A 2 kg mass is suspended from the spring and in equilibrium the extension of the spring is 0.05 m. Find the modulus of elasticity of the spring.

Solution

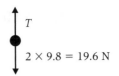

The diagram shows the forces acting on the mass. When it is in equilibrium, we have;

$$T = 2 \times 9.8$$
$$= 19.6 \text{ N}$$

Using Hooke's law this becomes;

$$\frac{\lambda \times 0.05}{0.5} = 19.6$$
$$\lambda = 196 \text{ N}$$

EXERCISE 2D

1 A spring has modulus of elasticity 40 N and natural length 0.8 m. A particle is attached to the end of the spring and the system is allowed to hang vertically. Find the extension of the spring when the particle is in equilibrium, if the mass of the particle is:

 (a) 2kg

 (b) 1.2 kg

 (c) 200 grams.

2 A spring has natural length 0.25 m and modulus of elasticity 20 N. A force of magnitude 40 N is applied to one end, while the other remains fixed. Find the extension of the spring when the forces are in equilibrium.

3 A spring has natural length 20 cm. When it supports a particle of mass 4 kg in equilibrium, it has an extension of 5 cm. Find the modulus of elasticity of the spring.

4 An elastic string has natural length 60 cm and modulus of elasticity 4 N. It stretches 10 cm when it supports an object with an unknown mass in equilibrium. Find the mass of the object.

5 Two identical springs have natural length 8 cm and modulus of elasticity 20 N. A 100 gram mass is attached to the springs so that it is in equilibrium.

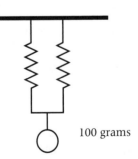

 (a) Find the extension of a single spring that supports the mass.

 (b) If the springs support the mass as shown in the diagram, find the extension of each spring.

 (c) If the springs are joined end to end and then support the mass, find the total extension of springs.

2.5 Energy and variable forces

So far our considerations have been restricted to forces that either remain constant or that are modelled as being constant. In this section you will consider how to extend the ideas previously encountered to variable forces.

If a force that has magnitude $f(x)$, where x is the displacement of the particle, acts on a particle, of mass m, then applying Newton's second law gives

$$f(x) = ma$$

In the chapter on kinetics and variable acceleration you saw that the acceleration can be expressed as $\dfrac{dv}{dt}$, but using the chain rule this can also be expressed as $\dfrac{dv}{dx} \times \dfrac{dx}{dt}$ or $v\dfrac{dv}{dx}$ and so the equation above could be written as

$$f(x) = mv\frac{dv}{dx}$$

Noting that as x changes from x_1 to x_2, the speed will change from u to v you can integrate to obtain

$$\int_{x_2}^{x_1} f(x)dx = m\int_u^v v\,dv$$

$$= m\left[\frac{1}{2}v^2\right]_u^v$$

$$= \frac{1}{2}mv^2 - \frac{1}{2}mu^2$$

This result shows that integrating $f(x)$ with respect to x will give the change in kinetic energy and the work done by a variable force is $\int f(x)dx$.

Elastic potential energy

When a spring is stretched, work is done. In the same way as when work is done lifting a body it gains potential energy, a stretched or compressed spring also has potential energy, that could be converted to kinetic energy if the spring is released.

Consider a spring. The tension in the spring is given by $T = \dfrac{\lambda x}{l}$.

If the spring is extended by a distance e from its natural length, then the work done will be given by

$$\int_0^e \frac{\lambda x}{l}dx = \left[\frac{\lambda x^2}{2l}\right]_0^e$$

$$= \frac{\lambda e^2}{2l}$$

As this is the work done in stretching the spring, you can also state that this is also the amount of potential energy stored in the spring. This is often expressed as follows.

> The elastic potential energy (EPE) of a stretched (or compressed) spring $= \dfrac{\lambda e^2}{2l}$.

The following examples show how this result can be applied.

Worked example 2.12

A spring has natural length 20 cm and modulus of elasticity 80 N. Calculate the work done in stretching the spring

(a) from its natural length to a length of 25 cm

(b) from a length of 30 cm to 40 cm.

Solution

(a) This is found by substituting $\lambda = 80$, $l = 0.2$ and $e = 0.05$ into the formula $\dfrac{\lambda e^2}{2l}$

$$\text{Work done} = \frac{80 \times 0.05^2}{2 \times 0.2}$$
$$= 0.5 \text{ J}$$

(b) The required amount is the work done to stretch the spring to 40 cm less the work done to stretch it to 30 cm. Note that the extensions will be 0.1 m and 0.2 m.

$$\text{Work done} = \frac{80 \times 0.2^2}{2 \times 0.2} - \frac{80 \times 0.1^2}{2 \times 0.2}$$
$$= 8 - 2$$
$$= 6 \text{ J}$$

Worked example 2.13

A ball, of mass 300 grams, is placed on top of a spring of natural length 10 cm and modulus of elasticity 80 N. The spring is compressed until its length is 5 cm and released. Find the maximum height of the ball above the base of the spring.

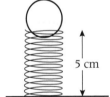

Solution

The initial energies can be calculated.

The EPE of the spring $\dfrac{80 \times 0.05^2}{2 \times 0.1} = 1 \text{ J}$

The gravitational potential energy of the ball is $0.3 \times 9.8 \times 0.05 = 0.147 \text{ J}$.

So the total initial energy of the ball is 1.147 J.

At its highest point the gravitational potential energy is $0.3 \times 9.8 \times h = 2.94h \text{ J}$.

If you assume that energy is conserved, then

$$2.94h = 1.147$$
$$h = \frac{1.147}{2.94} = 0.390 \text{ m (to 3 sf)}$$

Worked example 2.14

A sphere, of mass 200 grams, is attached to one end of an elastic string. The other end of the string is fixed to the point O. The string has natural length 50 cm and modulus of elasticity 4.9 N. The sphere is released from rest at O and falls vertically.

(a) Calculate the maximum distance between the sphere and O.

(b) Determine the maximum speed of the sphere.

Solution

(a) Initially the sphere will only have gravitational potential energy. Let e be equal to the extension of the string and assume that at its lowest point the sphere has no gravitational potential energy. Then the gravitational potential energy lost as the sphere falls is given by

$$0.2 \times 9.8 \times (0.5 + e) = 0.98 + 1.96e$$

When the particle comes to rest it has no kinetic energy, no potential energy and so has only elastic potential energy. So at its lowest point

$$\text{EPE} = \frac{4.9e^2}{2 \times 0.5}$$

$$= 4.9e^2$$

As energy is conserved the final EPE will be equal to the initial gravitational potential energy lost, so

$$0.98 + 1.96e = 4.9e^2$$
$$0 = 4.9e^2 - 1.96e - 0.98$$

Solving this quadratic equation gives two values of e

$$e = 0.690 \text{ m or } e = -0.290 \text{ m (to 3 sf)}$$

As the second of these does not apply, because $e \geq 0$, there is a maximum extension of 0.690 m.

The maximum distance between the sphere and the point of suspension is then

$$0.690 + 0.5 = 1.190 \text{ m}$$

(b) The sphere will reach its maximum speed when its acceleration becomes zero. This will happen when the sphere reaches its equilibrium position. After this the sphere will decelerate and slow down until it comes to rest.

First find the equilibrium position. If e is the extension of the spring at the equilibrium position, then

$$0.2 \times 9.8 = \frac{4.9e}{0.5}$$

$$e = \frac{0.98}{4.9} = 0.2 \text{ m}$$

Using this value for the extension of the string and v for the speed of the sphere

$$\text{EPE} = \frac{4.9 \times 0.2^2}{2 \times 0.5}$$

$$= 0.196 \, \text{J}$$

$$\text{KE} = \tfrac{1}{2} \times 0.2v^2$$

$$= 0.1v^2$$

$$\text{GPE lost} = 0.2 \times 9.8 \times (0.5 + 0.2)$$

$$= 1.372 \, \text{J}$$

As the total energy will remain equal to the initial energy of the system

$$1.372 = 0.196 + 0.1v^2$$
$$1.176 = 0.1v^2$$

Then solving for v gives

$$v = \sqrt{11.76}$$
$$= 3.43 \, \text{m s}^{-1} \, \text{(to 3 sf)}$$

EXERCISE 2E

1 An elastic spring has natural length 2.5 m and modulus of elasticity 100 N. Calculate the work done in extending it

(a) from 2.5 m to 2.7 m

(b) from 2.7 m to 2.9 m.

2 In a horizontal pinball machine the spring, which has natural length 20 cm, is compressed 5 cm. If the mass of the ball is 20 grams and the modulus of elasticity of the spring is 80 N. What is the speed of the ball when it leaves the spring assuming that friction can be neglected?

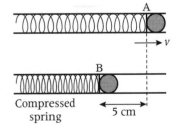

Ball leaves spring with speed v

3 A 100 gram mass is attached to the end B of an elastic string AB with modulus of elasticity of 3.92 N and natural length 0.25 m, the end A being fixed. The mass is pulled down from A until AB is 0.5 m and then released.

Find the velocity of the mass when the string first becomes slack and show that the mass comes to rest when it reaches A.

10 A 15 tonne wagon travelling at 3.6 m s^{-1} is brought to rest by a buffer (a spring) having a natural length of 1 m and modulus of elasticity of 7.5 × 10^5 N. Assuming that the wagon comes into contact with the buffer smoothly without rebound, calculate the compression of the buffer if there is a constant rolling friction force of 800 N.

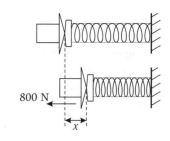

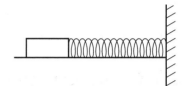

11 A 10 kg block rests on a rough horizontal table. The spring, which is not attached to the block, has a natural length of 0.8 m and modulus of elasticity 400 N. If the spring is compressed 0.2 m and then released from rest determine the velocity of the block when it has moved through 0.4 m. The coefficient of friction between the block and the table is 0.2.

12 A platform P has negligible mass and is tied down so that the 0.4 m long cords keep the spring compressed 0.6 m when nothing is on the platform. The modulus of elasticity of the spring is 200 N. If a 2 kg block is placed on the platform and released when the platform is pushed down 0.1 m, determine the velocity with which the block leaves the platform and the maximum height it subsequently reaches.

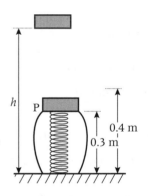

13 An archaeologist investigates the mechanics of large catapults used in sieges of castles. The diagram shows a simplified plan of such a catapult about to be fired horizontally.

The rock B of mass 20 kg is in the catapult as shown. Calculate the speed with which the rock is released at A when the elastic string returns to its natural length of 2 m if the string's modulus of elasticity is 500 N.

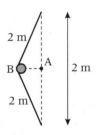

14 A ball B of mass m is attached to one end of a light elastic string of natural length a and modulus of $2mg$. The other end of the string is attached to a fixed point O. The ball is projected vertically upwards from O with speed $\sqrt{(8ga)}$; find the speed of the ball when OB = 2a.

Given that the string breaks when OB = 2a, find the speed of the ball when it returns to O. [A]

Worked example 2.16 ———————————————

Use Newton's universal law of gravitation to determine the value of g on the planet Mars.

The mass of Mars is 6.55×10^{23} kg and the radius of Mars is 3.36×10^6 m.

2

Solution

Calculate the gravitational force acting on a particle of mass m kg, taking $M = 6.55 \times 10^{23}$ and $d = 3.36 \times 10^6$.

$$F = \frac{6.67 \times 10^{-11} \times 6.55 \times 10^{23} \times m}{(3.36 \times 10^6)^2}$$

$$= 3.87m \text{ N}$$

As this must be equal to mg on Mars, we have $g = 3.87$ m s^{-2} on the planet Mars.

EXERCISE 2F ———————————————

1 A satellite, of mass 300 kg, orbits the Earth at a height of 7000 km above the surface of the Earth. Calculate the magnitude of the gravitational attraction that acts on the satellite.

2 The mass of the Moon is 7.38×10^{22} kg and the radius of the Moon is 1.73×10^6 m. Determine the acceleration due to gravity on the Moon.

3 A planet has a mass of 5×10^{20} kg and on this planet the acceleration due to gravity is 3.2 m s^{-1}. Determine the radius of the planet.

4 A man, of mass 80 kg, climbs 5000 m to the top of a mountain.

(a) Use the universal law of gravitation to calculate the gravitational attraction on the man.

(b) Compare your answer to part (a) with the result given by simply using mg.

5 The mass of the Sun is 1.99×10^{30} kg and the average distance between the centres of the Earth and the Sun is 1.47×10^7 km.

(a) Calculate the attractive force that the Sun exerts on the Earth.

(b) What force does the Earth exert on the Sun?

2.7 Work and the law of universal gravitation

You have used the result that the gravitational potential energy is given by mgh. This is satisfactory, but for large values of h you should treat gravity as a variable force and calculate the gravitational potential energy by integrating the expression for the gravitational attraction given in the law of universal gravitation.

For example to calculate the gravitational potential energy at a height h above the surface of the Earth you need to evaluate the integral

$$\int_r^{r+h} \frac{GMm}{x^2}\,dx$$

where r is the radius of the Earth.

Worked example 2.17

A climber, of mass 75 kg, climbs to the top of a mountain of height 2000 m above the surface of the Earth. Calculate the gravitational potential energy of the climber relative to the surface of the Earth.

Note that the radius of the Earth is 6.37×10^6 m and that its mass is 5.98×10^{24} kg. Also G is 6.67×10^{-11}.

Solution

The gravitational potential energy is given by

$$\int_r^{r+h} \frac{GMm}{x^2}\,dx = \left[-\frac{GMm}{x}\right]_r^{r+h}$$

$$= GMm\left(\frac{-1}{r+h} + \frac{1}{r}\right)$$

$$= \frac{GMmh}{r(r+h)}$$

Substituting the values of G, M, m, r and h gives

$$\frac{6.67 \times 10^{-11} \times 5.98 \times 10^{24} \times 75 \times 2000}{6.37 \times 10^6 (6.37 \times 10^6 + 2000)} = 1\,470\,000\,\text{J (to 3 sf)}$$

Note that $75 \times 9.8 \times 2000 = 1\,470\,000$ J (to 3 sf), so at this height there is no real need to consider gravity as a variable force.

Worked example 2.18

A satellite, of mass 400 kg, is to orbit the earth at a height of 3.6×10^7 m above the surface of the Earth, where it is to travel at 230 m s^{-1}. Find the work that must be done to position the satellite in this way.

Solution

First calculate the kinetic energy of the satellite.

$$\tfrac{1}{2} \times 400 \times 230^2 = 1.06 \times 10^7 \,\text{J (to 3 sf)}$$

Then consider the work done against gravity to raise the satellite to this height. We have the result below from the previous worked example.

$$\int_{r}^{r+h} \frac{GMm}{x^2}\, dx = \frac{GMmh}{r(r+h)}$$

Substituting $G = 6.67 \times 10^{-11}$, $M = 5.98 \times 10^{24}$, $m = 400$, $r = 6.37 \times 10^6$ and $h = 3.6 \times 10^7$, gives

$$\frac{6.67 \times 10^{-11} \times 5.98 \times 10^{24} \times 400 \times 3.6 \times 10^7}{6.37 \times 10^6(6.37 \times 10^6 + 3.6 \times 10^7)} = 2.13 \times 10^{10} \,\text{J (to 3 sf)}$$

Total work done $= 1.06 \times 10^7 + 6.38 \times 10^{10} = 2.13 \times 10^{10} \,\text{J}$ (to 3 sf)

EXERCISE 2G

1 A rocket rises to a height of 4×10^8 m above the surface of the Earth. Assume that the mass of the rocket remains constant at 500 kg. Calculate the gravitational potential energy of the rocket at this height relative to the surface of the Earth.

2 A climber, of mass 85 kg, reaches the top of Mount Everest at a height of 8850 m above sea level.

   (a) Calculate the gravitational potential energy of the climber relative to sea level.

   (b) Would it be reasonable to calculate the gravitational potential energy using mgh at this altitude?

3 A satellite, of mass 600 kg, is to be put into orbit at a height of 4.5×10^5 m above the surface of the Earth, where it should travel at $300 \,\text{m s}^{-1}$. Calculate the work that must be done to put the satellite into orbit in this way.

4 A mountain range on the planet Mars has a peak at a height of 5000 m above the surface of the planet. Find the gravitational potential energy, relative to the surface of the planet, of an alien who is on this peak. The mass of the alien is 120 kg.

   Note: the mass of Mars is 6.55×10^{23} kg and the radius of Mars is 3.36×10^6 m.

5 The work done for an object to escape from the Earth's gravitational influence can be calculated by assuming that the object reaches an infinite height. Calculate the work done in this way for a rocket of mass 2000 kg.

2.8 Power

Power is defined as the rate of doing work. For example we may talk about a more powerful car or motorbike. This is a way of describing how quickly they gain kinetic energy. The more quickly kinetic energy is gained, the shorter the time that the work is done in and so the more powerful the vehicle.

A simple definition of power is:

$$\text{Power} = \frac{\text{work done}}{\text{time taken}}.$$

Worked example 2.19

Hannah, who has mass 50 kg, climbs a flight of stairs in 20 seconds. As she climbs the stairs she rises a total of 4 m.

(a) Calculate the work done as she climbs the stairs.

(b) Calculate her power output as she climbs the stairs.

Solution

(a) Work done $= 50 \times 9.8 \times 4$
$= 1960 \text{ J}$

(b) Power $= \dfrac{\text{work done}}{\text{time taken}}$

$= \dfrac{1960}{20}$

$= 98 \text{ W}$

Note that the SI units for power are Watts (W). An alternative unit would be J s^{-1}. Another, more traditional, unit that is sometimes used for power is the horsepower (hp), and is such that 1 hp is approximately 740 watts.

Work done by force

An alternative approach to power is to derive a formula based on the definition that power is the rate of doing work.

The work done by a force is Fs, where F is the magnitude of the force and s is the displacement. As rates can found by differentiating with respect to t, we have

$$\text{Power} = \frac{d}{dt}(Fs).$$

Considering the case of a constant force leads to

$$\text{Power} = \frac{d}{dt}(Fs)$$

$$= F\frac{ds}{dt}$$

$$= Fv$$

This result is very useful and can be applied in many examples.

Worked example 2.20

A car experiences a resistance force of magnitude 1200 N, when travelling at a constant speed of 25 m s^{-1}. Calculate the power output of the car.

Solution

As the car is travelling at a constant speed, there must be a forward force on the car equal in magnitude to the resistance force. So in this case the force F exerted by the car has magnitude 1200 N and $v = 25$ m s^{-1}. Using $P = Fv$, gives

$$P = 1200 \times 25$$
$$= 30\,000 \text{ W}$$

Worked example 2.21

A car, of mass 1200 kg, experiences a resistance force that is proportional to its speed. The car has a maximum power output of 36 000 W and a maximum speed of 40 m s^{-1}.

(a) Determine an expression for the magnitude of the resistance force, when the speed of the car is v m s^{-1}.

(b) Find the power output if the car is accelerating at 2 m s^{-2} and is travelling at 10 m s^{-1}.

(c) Calculate the maximum acceleration of the car when it is travelling at 20 m s^{-1}.

Solution

(a) As the resistance is proportional to the speed we have

$$R = kv.$$

At its top speed the resistance force will be equal in magnitude to the forward force exerted by the car. Using $P = Fv$ gives

$$36\,000 = 40k \times 40$$
$$k = \frac{36\,000}{40^2}$$
$$= 22.5$$

(b) The car exerts a forward, of magnitude F N, and experiences a resistive force of magnitude 22.5×10. So the resultant force on the car is $F - 225$. As the car is accelerating at 2 m s^{-2}, you can apply Newton's second law to give

$$F - 225 = 1200 \times 2$$
$$F = 2625 \text{ N}$$

Now the power output can be found using $P = Fv$ as

$$P = 2625 \times 10$$
$$= 26\,250 \text{ W}$$

Using $P = Fv$ gives

$$32\,000 = (840 + 20v)v$$
$$20v^2 + 840v - 32\,000 = 0$$
$$v^2 + 42v - 1600 = 0$$

Solving this quadratic gives:

$$v = \frac{-42 \pm \sqrt{42^2 - 4 \times 1 \times (-1600)}}{2 \times 1}$$
$$= 24.2 \text{ or } -66.2 \text{ m s}^{-1}$$

So the maximum speed up the slope is 24.2 m s^{-1}.

(c) If the car is travelling at 5 m s^{-1}, then there will be a resistance force of 100 N:

$$F - 100 = 1200 \times 2$$
$$= 2500 \text{ N}$$

The power can then be found using $P = Fv$:

$$P = 2500 \times 5$$
$$= 12\,500 \text{ W}$$

EXERCISE 2H

1 A crane lifts a load, of mass 800 kg, through a height of 12 m in 2 minutes.

   (a) Calculate the work done by the crane.

   (b) Find the power of the crane.

2 A child, of mass 56 kg, climbs up a flight of stairs in 49 seconds. There are 50 steps, each of height 18 cm. Calculate the rate at which the child was working as she climbed the stairs.

3 A train travels at a constant speed of 30 m s^{-1} and experiences a resistance force of magnitude 30 000 N at this speed. Calculate the power output of the train.

4 A pump is used to raise water from ground level into a tank at a height of 5m. The pump is able to pump 5000 litres per hour. Find the power of the pump. (The mass of 1 litre of water is 1 kg.)

5 A car, of mass 1000 kg, has a maximum power output of 36000 W and a maximum speed of 40 m s^{-1}. The resistance force on the car is proportional to its speed.

   (a) Find the magnitude of the resistance force when it is travelling at its maximum speed.

   (b) Find the magnitude of the resistance force when the car is travelling at 30 m s^{-1}.

   (c) Find the maximum possible acceleration of the car when it is travelling at 30 m s^{-1}.

10 A car, of mass 1000 kg, is assumed to experience a resistance force that is proportional to its speed squared. The car has a maximum power output of 32 000 W and a top speed of 40 m s^{-1}, on the horizontal.

(a) Find the resistance force acting when the car travels at a speed of 20 m s^{-1}.

(b) The car travels 500 m up a slope inclined at an angle α to the horizontal, where $\sin \alpha = \frac{1}{15}$. The car travels at a constant speed of 20 m s^{-1}. Find the work done by the car as it travels up the slope.

11 A cyclist can pedal up a slope, inclined at 4° to the horizontal, at a maximum speed of 2 m s^{-1}. Model the cycle as a particle of mass 70 kg. Assume that there are no resistance forces acting on the cyclist.

(a) When he is pedalling up the slope at his maximum speed, show that the power output of the cyclist is approximately 96 W.

(b) If the power output remains the same, find the maximum speed of the cyclist when travelling up a slope inclined at 6° to the horizontal.

(c) (i) When modelling the motion uphill, explain why it is reasonable to assume that there is no resistance.

(ii) When trying to find the maximum speed of the cyclist down the slope, explain why it is **not** reasonable to assume that there is no resistance. [A]

12 A car, of mass 1200 kg, has a maximum power output of 48 000 W. On a horizontal road the car has a maximum speed of 40 m s^{-1}. Assume that the resistance forces acting on the car are proportional to its speed.

(a) Find the resistance force acting on the car when it travels at v m s^{-1}.

(b) Find the percentage reduction in the power output of the car if its speed is reduced by 10%.

(c) Use your answer to part **(b)** to describe one advantage of reducing the speed at which the car is driven.

(d) Find the maximum speed of the car, when being driven up a slope at 4° to the horizontal. [A]

13 The maximum power output of a car is 50 000 W and its top speed, on a horizontal road, is 40 m s^{-1}. In order to model the motion of the car, assume that it experiences a resistance force proportional to its speed.

   (a) Find the resistance force when the car is travelling at 20 m s^{-1}.

   (b) When the car tows a caravan the resistance force is increased by 50%. Find the maximum speed of the car when it tows the caravan on a horizontal road.   [A]

14 A car and its driver, of a total mass 500 kg, are ascending a hill of inclination $\sin^{-1}\left(\frac{1}{7}\right)$ to the horizontal with a constant speed of 5 m s^{-1}. Given that the motion is opposed by a frictional force of magnitude 800 N, find the power generated by the engine of the car.

The driver presses the accelerator, which has the effect of suddenly increasing the power to 20 kW. Calculate the resulting acceleration of the car.   [A]

15 A car, of mass 1000 kg, travels up a hill inclined at 4° to the horizontal. Assume that the car experiences a constant resistance force, and is moving at constant or increasing speed.

   (a) Draw and label a diagram to show the forces acting on the car, if it is modelled as a particle. Describe one weakness of modelling the car as a particle.

   (b) If the car exerts a forward force of 1000 N when travelling at a constant speed of 20 m s^{-1} up the hill, show that the magnitude of the resistance force is 316 N to the nearest Newton.

   (c) Use your answer to part **(b)** to find the power output of the car if it is travelling at 20 m s^{-1} and accelerating at 1.5 m s^{-2}.   [A]

Key point summary

I The kinetic energy of a body is defined as $\frac{1}{2}mv^2$.   *p24*

2 The work done by the force is the quantity *Fs*.   *p26*

3 Gravitational potential energy = *mgh*.   *p32*

4 Hooke's law states that the tension *T* is   *p38*
given by $\dfrac{\lambda x}{l}$.

5 The elastic potential energy (EPE) of a stretched   *p41*
or compressed spring $= \dfrac{\lambda e^2}{2l}$.

6 Power $= \dfrac{\text{work done}}{\text{time taken}}$ (Rate of doing work).   *p50*

Formulae to learn

Kinetic energy	$\frac{1}{2}mv^2$
Work done	Fs or $Fs \cos \theta$
Work done = change in kinetic energy	
Gravitational potential energy	mgh
Hooke's law	$T = \dfrac{\lambda x}{l}$
Work done by a variable force	$\int f(x)dx$
Elastic potential energy	$\dfrac{\lambda e^2}{2l}$
Power	$P = Fv$

Test yourself	**What to review**

1 Calculate the gain in kinetic energy as a car, of mass 1200 kg, increases in speed from 10 to 25 m s^{-1}.

Section 2,1

2 A force of 500 N acts on a car, of mass 1250 kg, in the direction of motion. The car has an initial speed of 8 m s^{-1}. The force acts as the car travels 25 m on a horizontal surface.

Section 2.2

   (a) Calculate the work done by the force as the car travels this distance.

   (b) Find the final speed of the car.

3 A go-kart, of mass 50 kg, is at rest at the top of a slope inclined at 8° to the horizontal. Find the speed of the go-kart when it has travelled 70 m down the slope

Section 2.3

   (a) if there is no resistance to the motion,

   (b) there is a constant 20 N resistance force.

4 A 'dropslide' at a leisure park consists of a curved section *AB* and a horizontal section *BC* shown below. Children start at rest at the point *A* and slide down to *B* and on towards *C*. The points, *A*, *B* and *C* all lie in the same vertical plane and the motion of the child is in this plane.

Section 2.3

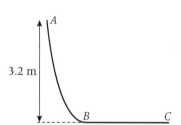

A child of mass 30 kg uses the slide.

   (a) Assuming that there is no friction or air resistance acting on the child on the section *AB*, find the speed of the child at *B*. How would this speed compare with that of a heavier child?

   (b) If the child travels 5 m along *BC* before stopping, find the magnitude of the friction force between the child and the surface. State two factors that would influence the magnitude of this force for different children. [A]

Test yourself *(continued)*	**What to review**

5 A sphere, of mass 500 grams, is attached to an elastic string
of natural length 70 cm and modulus of elasticity 70 N.
One end of the string is fixed to a point *O*.

   (a) Find the length of the elastic when the sphere hangs in
equilibrium.

The sphere is released from the point *O*.

   (b) Find the maximum distance between the sphere and *O*.

   (c) Find the speed of the sphere when the length of the
elastic string is 80 cm.

   (d) Find the maximum speed of the sphere.

Section 2.5

---

6 Calculate the work done against gravity in raising a rocket,
of mass 400 kg, from ground level to a height of 50 000 m.

Section 2.7

---

7 A car of maximum power output 32 kW and mass 800 kg,
is travelling up a slope at an angle θ to the horizontal.

A simple model for the motion of the car assumes that there
are no resistance forces acting on the car.

   (a) Find the angle θ, to the nearest degree, for the steepest
slope that the car can ascend at a speed of 10 m s^{-1}.

A refined model for the motion of the car would take account .
of the resistance forces on the car.

   (b) The slope is in fact at 5° to the horizontal, and the car is
still travelling at its maximum speed of 10 m s^{-1}.
Find the magnitude of the resistance forces on the car.

   (c) The resistance forces on the car are assumed to be
proportional to the speed. Use your result to part **(b)** to
find a simple model for the resistance forces.

Section 2.8

[A]

Test yourself **ANSWERS**

1 315 000 J.

2 (a) 12 500 J,   **(b)** 9.17 m s^{-1}.

3 (a) 13.8 m s^{-1},   **(b)** 11.6 m s^{-1}.

4 (a) 7.92 m s^{-1}, same,   **(b)** 188 N, mass, clothes.

5 (a) 74.9 cm,   **(b)** 1.015 m,   **(c)** 3.70 m s^{-1},   **(d)** 3.77 m s^{-1}.

6 1.95×10^8 J.

7 (a) 24°,   **(b)** 2517 N,   **(c)** $252v$ N.

CHAPTER 3

Circular motion

Learning objectives

After studying this chapter you should be able to:

- convert from rpm to rad s^{-1}
- know that the velocity is directed along the tangent of the circle
- know that the acceleration is directed towards the centre of the circle
- know that $v = r\omega$
- know that $a = r\omega^2 = \dfrac{v^2}{r}$
- solve problems for motion in horizontal or vertical circles at constant speeds.

3.1 Introduction

This chapter will focus on the motion of objects that travel in a circle with constant speed. There are many everyday situations which can be modelled in this way, for example, fairground rides, satellites orbiting the Earth and clothes in a spindrier. Also cars travelling around corners or on roundabouts travel round part of a circle. To analyse such situations we need to apply Newton's second law after finding the resultant force along with the acceleration of the object travelling round the circle. Before doing this you must be familiar with the concept of angular speed.

3.2 Angular speed

Imagine a line drawn from the centre of the circle to the object that is travelling round the circle. The rate at which this line rotates about the centre is called the angular speed of the object. This could be given in terms of rpm (revolutions per minute), as with car engines, but it is most often given in radians per second (rad s^{-1}).

We will now consider an example that makes use of angular speed. To do this you will need to recall that one complete revolution is equivalent to turning through 2π radians.

$$1 \text{ rpm} = \frac{2\pi}{60} \text{ rad s}^{-1}$$

3

Worked example 3.1

The angular speed of a record is given as $33\frac{1}{3}$ rpm. Find the angular speed of the record in radians per second.

Solution

In one revolution there are 2π radians.

So $33\frac{1}{3}$ r.p.m. $= 33\frac{1}{3} \times 2\pi$ radians per minute

$$= \frac{33\frac{1}{3} \times 2\pi}{60} \text{ radians per second}$$

$$= \frac{10\pi}{9}$$

$$= 3.49 \text{ rad s}^{-1}$$

Velocity and circular motion

Consider now a particle, which moves with angular speed ω rad s^{-1}. The angle turned through in 1 second will be ω radians, so the angle turned through in t seconds will be $\theta = \omega t$ radians. If the particle moves in a circle with radius r m, the distance moved by the particle will be the length of the arc AB.

$$AB = r\theta$$

Each second the particle moves a distance $r\omega$, so the speed, v, of the particle is given by

$$v = r\omega$$

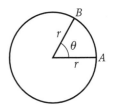

The velocity has magnitude $r\omega$ and is directed along a tangent to the circle.

Acceleration and circular motion

Newton's first law of motion states that a particle will move in a straight line unless acted upon by a force. Therefore, if a particle moves in a circle, there must be a force acting upon it. If the speed is constant then the resultant force will have no component in the direction of motion. Hence the resultant force on the particle will be perpendicular to the velocity and must always act towards the centre. Consequently, if the resultant force is towards the centre, then so is the acceleration of the particle. You will now find the magnitude of this acceleration.

Suppose a particle moves in a circle with centre O, radius r, and with constant angular velocity ω.

Suppose further that the particle starts from A$(t = 0)$ so $\theta = \omega t$. The position vector of the particle **OP**, in terms of the unit vectors **i** and **j** will be given by

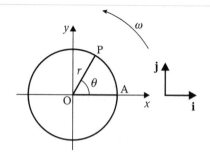

$$\mathbf{r} = x\mathbf{i} + y\mathbf{j}$$
$$= r \cos \theta \mathbf{i} + r \sin \theta \mathbf{j}$$
$$= r \cos \omega t \, \mathbf{i} + r \sin \omega t \, \mathbf{j}$$

If you differentiate once you get the velocity vector and twice you get the acceleration vector.

$$\mathbf{v} = - \omega r \sin \omega t \, \mathbf{i} + \omega r \cos \omega t \, \mathbf{j}$$

and

$$\mathbf{a} = - \omega^2 r \cos \omega t \, \mathbf{i} - \omega^2 r \sin \omega t \, \mathbf{j}$$

The magnitude of the acceleration of the particle is:

$$a = \omega^2 r \sqrt{\cos^2 \omega t + \sin^2 \omega t}$$

But $\cos^2 \theta + \sin^2 \theta \equiv 1$, so

$$a = r\omega^2$$

Sometimes it is useful to express the magnitude of the acceleration in terms of the speed, v, rather than ω. From $v = r\omega$, note that $\omega = \dfrac{v}{r}$ and substitute this so that the expression for the magnitude of the acceleration becomes

$$a = r\left(\frac{v}{r}\right)^2 = \frac{v^2}{r}$$

To confirm that the direction of the particle's acceleration is towards the centre compare the acceleration and position vectors.

$$\mathbf{a} = - \omega^2 \, (r \cos \omega t \, \mathbf{i} + r \sin \omega t \, \mathbf{j})$$
$$\mathbf{a} = - \omega^2 \mathbf{r}$$

The position vector is directed outwards from the centre of the circle. The acceleration is in the opposite direction and so is directed **towards** the centre.

Worked example 3.2

If the radius of the Earth is taken as 6370 km find the speed and magnitude of the acceleration of a man standing on the Equator.

$$\omega = 1 \text{ rev per day}$$

$$= \frac{2\pi}{24 \times 60 \times 60} = 7.27 \times 10^{-5} \text{ rad s}^{-1}$$

$$v = 6\,370\,000 \times 7.27 \times 10^{-5} \text{ m s}^{-1} = 463 \text{ m s}^{-1}$$

$$a = 637\,000 \times (7.27 \times 10^{-5})^2 = 3.37 \times 10^{-2} \text{ m s}^{-2}$$

EXERCISE 3A

1 What is the angular speed of the minute hand of a clock in

  (a) revolutions per minute **(b)** radians per second.

2 A wheel makes 100 revolutions in 10 minutes. Find its angular speed in radians per second.

3 The distance of the Moon from the Earth is approximately 355 000 km. Estimate the speed of the Moon relative to the Earth in m s^{-1}. (Assume that the Moon rotates round the Earth twice a day in a circular orbit.)

4 The distance from the Sun to the Earth is approximately 150×10^5 km. Estimate the speed of the Earth relative to the Sun. (Assume that the orbit of the Earth is a circle and that the Earth orbits the Sun once every year.)

5 Find the speed and the magnitude of the acceleration of a particle, which moves in a circle with radius 20 cm, and angular speed of 2500 rpm.

6 Find the magnitude of the resultant force on a particle of mass 250 grams, which moves in a circle of radius 10 m and angular speed of 36 rpm.

7 A particle moves in a circle with speed 5 m s^{-1}. Given that the acceleration has magnitude 10 m s^{-2}, find the radius of the circle.

8 What is the magnitude of the acceleration of a truck, which goes round a bend of radius 20 m at a speed of 20 km/h.

9 A washing machine spins at 1000 rpm. The drum has diameter 40 cm. What are the speed and magnitude of the acceleration of a sock, which is stuck to the edge of the drum during the spinning cycle?

10 Joe and Tom ride on a fairground roundabout. Joe is 2 m and Tom is 1.5 m from the centre of rotation and the roundabout is rotating at 10 rpm. Find:

  (a) the angular speed of the roundabout in rad s^{-1}

  (b) the speeds of Joe and Tom in m s^{-1}.

3.3 Forces involved in horizontal circular motion

In the previous section you saw that when a particle, of mass m, moves in a circle with constant speed, its acceleration is of magnitude $r\omega^2$ (or v^2/r) and acts towards the centre of the circle (where r is the radius of the circle, v is the speed of the particle and ω is its angular speed). The resultant force, therefore, must always act towards the centre. Newton's second law implies that the magnitude of the resultant force will be given by

$$F = mr\omega^2 \qquad (\text{or } mv^2/r)$$

If the circle of motion is horizontal then any vertical components of force must cancel.

> When a particle moves in a horizontal circle with constant speed there are two principles that can always be applied:
>
> ■ resultant of vertical components of forces must be zero
> ■ '$F = ma$' can be applied radially.

Worked example 3.3

A particle P, of mass 100 grams, is attached to one end of a light inextensible string of length 50 cm. The other end of the string is fixed at O, on a smooth horizontal surface. The particle moves in a circle, with centre O, at 180 rpm. Find the tension in the string.

Solution

The diagram shows the forces acting on the particle, its weight, the normal reaction from the surface and the tension in the string.

The acceleration of P is horizontal, so the resultant of the vertical forces must be zero.

$$R = 0.98 \text{ N}$$

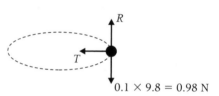

The angular speed must be converted from rpm to rad s^{-1}.

$$\omega = 180 \text{ rpm}$$

$$= 180 \times \frac{2\pi}{60} \text{ rad s}^{-1}$$

$$= 6\pi \text{ rad s}^{-1}$$

Using $F = ma$ in the radial direction gives

$$T = 0.1 \times 0.5 \times (6\pi)^2$$
$$= 17.8 \text{ N}$$

Worked example 3.4

A turntable rotates at $33\frac{1}{3}$ rpm. A counter, of mass 10 grams, is placed 10 cm from the centre of the circle and does not slip. Find the minimum possible value of the coefficient of friction.

Solution

The diagram shows the forces acting on the counter.

First express the angular speed in rad s^{-1}.

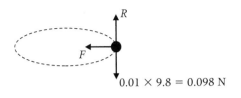

0.01 × 9.8 = 0.098 N

$$\omega = \frac{33\frac{1}{3} \times 2\pi}{60}$$

$$= \frac{10\pi}{9} \text{ rad s}^{-1}$$

Using $F = ma$ radially with $a = r\omega^2$

$$F = 0.01 \times 0.1 \left(\frac{10\pi}{9}\right)^2$$

$$= 0.01218 \text{ N}$$

Resolving vertically

$$R = 0.01 \times 9.8 = 0.098 \text{ N}$$

Then we can use the friction inequality $F \leqslant \mu R$, to give

$$0.01218 \leqslant \mu \times 0.098$$

$$\mu \geqslant 0.124 \text{ (to 3 sf)}$$

So the least value of μ is 0.124.

EXERCISE 3B

1 A particle, of mass 2 kg, is attached to a fixed point on a smooth horizontal table by a light inextensible string of length 50 cm. The particle travels in a circle on the table at 400 rpm. Find the tension in the string.

2 A particle, of mass 2 kg, is moving in a circle of radius 5 m with a constant speed of 3 m s^{-1}. What is the magnitude and direction of the resultant force acting on the particle?

3 A particle, of mass 3 kg, moves in a circle on a smooth horizontal plane. The particle is attached to a fixed point, O, on the plane, by a light inextensible string of length 1.5 m. If the velocity of the particle is 6 m s^{-1}, find the tension in the string.

4 An inextensible string has length 3 m. It is fixed at one end to a point O on a smooth horizontal table. A particle of mass 2 kg is attached to the other end and describes circles on the table with O as centre and the string taut. If the string breaks when the tension is 90 N, what is the maximum safe speed of the particle?

5 A marble is made to rotate against the outside rim of a circular tray of radius 0.2 m. The mass of the marble is 100 grams and it moves at 2 m s^{-1}. Calculate the horizontal force that the tray exerts on the marble.

6 An athlete throwing the hammer swings it in preparation for his throw. Assume that the hammer travels in a horizontal circle of radius 2.0 m and is rotating at 1 revolution per second. The mass of the wire is negligible and the mass of the hammer is 7.3 kg. What is the tension in the wire attached to the hammer? (Ignore the weight of the hammer.)

7 A particle moves with constant angular speed around a circle of radius a and centre O. The only force acting on the particle is directed towards O and is of magnitude $\dfrac{k}{a^2}$ per unit mass, where k is a constant. Find, in terms of k and a, the time taken for the particle to make one complete revolution.

8 A satellite, of mass 1 tonne, orbits a planet at 1 revolution per day. The satellite is at a height of 700 km above the surface of the planet. The radius of the planet is 6500 km. Find the force of gravity on the satellite.

9 A car, of mass 1 tonne, takes a bend, of radius 150 m, on a level road, at 80 km/h, without sliding. Find the frictional force between the tyres and the ground. What is the least value of μ?

10 Two particles, P and Q, are connected by a light inextensible string, that passes through a hole in a smooth horizontal table. Particle P has mass m and travels in a circle, whereas Q hangs in equilibrium under the table and has mass $2m$. If the radius of the circle in which P moves is 50 cm, find the angular velocity of P.

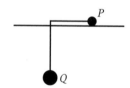

11 A horizontal turntable rotates at 45 rpm. A coin, of mass 50 grams, is placed on the turntable, at a distance 20 cm from the centre of rotation. The coefficient of friction between the coin and the turntable is 0.1.

   (a) Describe what happens to the coin.

   (b) What is the greatest distance from the centre of rotation that the coin can be placed without slipping?

   (c) How would your answers to parts **(b)** and **(c)** change for a heavier coin?

12 A penny, of mass m kg, is placed on the turntable of a record player 0.1 m from the centre. The turntable rotates at 45 rpm. If the penny is on the point of slipping, calculate the coefficient of friction between the penny and the turntable. Calculate the resultant force acting on the penny, when the turntable is rotating at 33 rpm.

13 The position vector **r** (metres), of a particle P at time t seconds, is given by

$$\mathbf{r} = 2\cos 3t\,\mathbf{i} + 2\sin 3t\,\mathbf{j}$$

where unit vectors **i** and **j** are perpendicular. The mass of the particle is 4 kg.

(a) Show that the particle moves with constant speed.

(b) Find the speed of P.

(c) Find the angular speed of P.

(d) Find the resultant force on P.

14 A car travels without slipping at $10\,\text{m s}^{-1}$ around a horizontal bend of radius 30 m. Find the least value of the coefficient of friction.

15 The coefficient of friction between a road surface and the tyres on a car is 0.9. A horizontal bend on the road has a radius of 40 m. Find the maximum speed that the car can take the bend without sliding.

16 A fairground ride consists of a rotating cylinder. People stand on the inside of the cylinder with their backs to it. When the speed of rotation is great enough the floor is lowered so that only friction stops them from falling. The diameter of the cylinder is 10 m. The coefficient of friction between a body and the cylinder is taken as 0.5. Find the least angular speed necessary to stop the body from falling.

17 A child sits on a roundabout at a distance of 5 m from the centre of rotation and at a height of 2 m above ground level. The roundabout completes one revolution every 2 seconds. After one revolution the child drops a small toy, of mass 500 grams, that she was carrying, which then falls to the ground without hitting the roundabout.

(a) Find the acceleration of the child on the roundabout and the magnitude of the force exerted on the toy by the child, before she drops it.

(b) Find the time that it takes for the toy to fall to the ground.

(c) Sketch a graph to show how the magnitude of the acceleration of the toy varies with time. Assume $t = 0$ one revolution before the toy is dropped.　　　　[A]

18 A strip of smooth metal, in the shape of a semi-circle of radius 20 cm is fixed on a smooth horizontal surface. A marble of mass 20 grams is fired into the semi-circle and travels at a speed of 5 m s^{-1}. Part of the path of the marble is shown by the dashed line in the diagram.

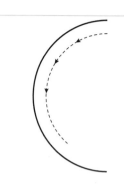

  (a) Find the magnitude of the acceleration of the marble in m s^{-2}.

  (b) Show that the magnitude of the resultant of the reaction forces acting on the marble is approximately 2.51 N.

  (c) Copy the diagram and show the path of the marble when it leaves the semi-circle. [A]

19 A device in a fun-fair consists of a hollow circular cylinder of radius 3 m, with a horizontal floor and vertical sides. A small child stands inside the cylinder and against the vertical side. The cylinder is rotated about its vertical axis of symmetry.

When the cylinder is rotating at a steady angular speed of 30 rev/min the floor of the cylinder is lowered, so that the child is in contact only with the vertical side.

Given that the child does not slip, find, correct to two decimal places, the minimum coefficient of friction between the child and the side. [A]

20 A traffic roundabout has a radius of 80 m. The road surface at the roundabout is horizontal.

  (a) Find the magnitude of the resultant force that acts on a car, of mass 1200 kg, travelling round the roundabout at 20 m s^{-1}.

Assume that the only horizontal force that acts on the car is friction. The coefficient of friction between the tyres and the road is μ.

  (b) Find an inequality that μ must satisfy for the car to follow a circular path round the roundabout.

Typical values of μ for road vehicles are between 0.6 and 0.8.

  (c) Calculate a safe speed limit for the roundabout.

  (d) What factor have your omitted from your calculation that would have reduced the speed limit found in part **(c)**? [A]

21 A car of mass 1.2 tonnes is travelling around a roundabout, at a steady speed of 12 m s^{-1}. The friction force that is acting on the car has a magnitude equal to 90% of the magnitude of the normal reaction on the car. Assume that the car can be modelled as a particle and that the road surface is horizontal.

(a) Draw a diagram to show the forces acting on the car if there is assumed to be no air resistance.

(b) Find the radius of the circle described by the car as it travels around the roundabout.

(c) The diagram shows the air resistance force that actually acts on the car as it moves on the roundabout, but that has been ignored in parts **(a)** and **(b)**.

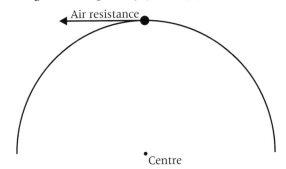

On a copy of the diagram draw a vector to show the resultant force on the car, and hence a vector to show the direction of the friction force on the car (i.e. the force between the tyres and the road).   [A]

3.4 Further circular motion

In this section you will consider examples of circular motion in situations where the forces acting are not just horizontal and vertical. The first of these examples is a simple situation, known as the conical pendulum.

Conical pendulum

Consider a particle, of mass m kg, which is suspended from a fixed point A by a light, inextensible string of length l. If the particle moves in a horizontal circle, then the string describes the curved surface of a cone.

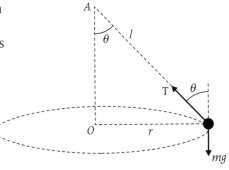

The centre of the circle O will be vertically below A. The radius of the circle will be $l \sin \theta$, where θ is the angle between the string and the vertical.

Using $F = ma$ radially:
$$T \sin \theta = mr\omega^2$$
or
$$T \sin \theta = ml \sin \theta\, \omega^2$$
$$T = ml\omega^2$$

Resolving vertically:
$$T \cos \theta = mg$$

From these two expressions it is possible to eliminate T to give

$$\cos \theta = \frac{mg}{ml\omega^2} = \frac{g}{l\omega^2}.$$

Note from this result that the angle does not depend on the mass. It also allows us to predict the angle for various combinations of l and ω.

Worked example 3.5

A ball, of mass 400 grams, is attached to one end of a light inelastic string of length 0.75 cm. The other end of the string is fixed to a point A. The ball moves in a horizontal circle, at 120 rpm. Find the tension in the string and the angle between the string and the vertical.

Solution

The diagram shows the forces acting on the ball.

First convert the angular speed to rad s⁻¹.

$$\omega = \frac{120 \times 2\pi}{60} = 4\pi \text{ rad s}^{-1}$$

Using $F = ma$ radially gives

$$T \sin \theta = 0.4 \times 0.75 \sin \theta \times (4\pi)^2$$
$$T = 47.37 \text{ N}$$

Resolving vertically

$$T \cos \theta = 0.4g$$
$$\cos \theta = \frac{0.4 \times 9.8}{47.37}$$
$$\theta = 85.3°$$

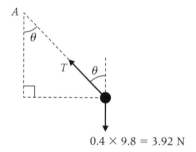

0.4 × 9.8 = 3.92 N

Worked example 3.6

A particle P, of mass m, is connected to two light inextensible strings of equal length l. The other ends of the strings are attached to fixed points A and B, a distance l apart with A vertically above B. The particle P rotates in a horizontal circle with angular speed ω, and both strings taut. Find the tension in each string and show that

$$\omega^2 > \frac{2g}{l}$$

Solution

The diagram shows the two tensions that act, along with the weight of the particle.

Using $F = ma$ radially gives

$$T_1 \sin 60° + T_2 \sin 60° = ml \sin 60° \omega^2$$
$$T_1 + T_2 = ml\omega^2$$

Resolving vertically gives

$$T_1 \cos 60° = T_2 \cos 60° + mg$$
$$T_1 - T_2 = 2mg.$$

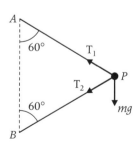

You now have a pair of simultaneous equations which when added give

$$2T_1 = ml\omega^2 + 2mg$$
$$T_1 = mg + \tfrac{1}{2}ml\omega^2$$

Subtracting the equations gives

$$2T_2 = ml\omega^2 - 2mg$$
$$T_2 = \tfrac{1}{2}ml\omega^2 - mg$$

So the tensions in the strings are functions of m, g and ω. In particular the tension in the top string is positive for all values of ω, but this is not the case in the lower string. If the angular speed is not great enough the lower string becomes slack. Hence if both strings are taut

$$T_2 > 0$$
$$\tfrac{1}{2}ml\omega^2 - mg > 0$$
$$\omega^2 > 2\frac{g}{l}$$

Worked example 3.7

A sphere P, of mass m, moves in a horizontal circle, with angular velocity ω, on the inside, smooth surface of an inverted cone, of semi-vertical angle α as shown. Find the radius of the circle in terms of α, ω and g.

Solution

The diagram shows the two forces acting on the sphere, which are modelled as a particle. These forces are the weight and the normal reaction, which is perpendicular to the surface of the cone.

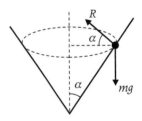

Resolving vertically gives

$$R \sin \alpha = mg$$

Using $F = ma$ radially gives

$$R \cos \alpha = mr\omega^2$$

These two expressions can then be divided as below

$$\frac{R \sin \alpha}{R \cos \alpha} = \frac{mg}{mr\omega^2}$$

$$\tan \alpha = \frac{g}{r\omega^2}$$

Now rearrange to make r the subject of this expression.

$$r = \frac{g}{\omega^2 \tan \alpha}$$

Worked example 3.8

An aircraft banks as it turns in a horizontal circle of radius
500 m. If the speed of the aircraft is 300 km h^{-1}, find the angle to
the horizontal at which the aircraft must be banked.

Solution

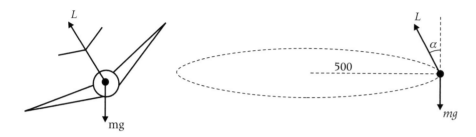

To model this situation assume that the lift force acts through
the centre of gravity of the aircraft. The aircraft can thus be
treated as a particle. The diagram shows the forces acting on the
aeroplane.

Resolving vertically gives

$$L \cos \alpha = mg$$

Using $F = ma$ radially gives

$$L \sin \alpha = m \times \frac{v^2}{500}$$

Where $v = 300$ km h$^{-1} = \dfrac{300 \times 1000}{3600 \text{ m s}^{-1}} = 83.3$ m s^{-1}

Dividing both equations and substituting for v gives

$$\frac{\cos \alpha}{\sin \alpha} = \frac{500g}{v^2} = \frac{500 \times 9.8}{83.3^2} = 0.706$$

$\tan \alpha = 1.42$
$\alpha = 55°$ to the nearest degree.

EXERCISE 3C

1 A particle, of mass 2 kg, is attached to a fixed point, A, by a
   light inextensible string of length l m, which is inclined at an
   angle θ to the vertical. The particle moves in a horizontal
   circle with speed v m s^{-1} and angular speed ω. The tension in
   the string is T N.

   (a) If $l = 0.5$ m and $\theta = 20°$, find T and ω.

   (b) If $l = 1$ m and $\omega = 5$ rad s^{-1}, find T and θ.

   (c) If $v = 2$ m s^{-1} and $\theta = 60°$, find l and T.

2 A particle, of mass 2 kg, is attached to a fixed point, *A*, by a light inextensible string of length 50 cm. The particle moves in a horizontal circle of radius 10 cm. Find the tension in the string and the particle's angular speed.

3 A particle, of mass 3 kg, is attached to a fixed point, *A*, by an inelastic string of length 70 cm. The particle moves in a horizontal circle with angular speed of 60 rpm. Find the tension in the string and the radius of the circle.

4 A particle, *P*, of mass 4 kg, is attached by a light inextensible string, of length 3 m, to a fixed point. The particle moves in a horizontal circle with an angular speed of 2 rad s^{-1}. Calculate:

   (a) the tension in the string

   (b) the angle the string makes with the vertical

   (c) the radius of the circle.

5 A particle, of mass 5 kg, is attached to a fixed point by a string of length 1 m. It describes horizontal circles of radius 0.5 m. Calculate the tension in the string and the speed of the particle.

6 A bead, of mass *m*, is threaded on a string of length 8 m, which is light and inextensible. The free ends of the string are attached to two fixed points separated vertically by a distance, which is half the length of the string, the lower fixed point being on a smooth, horizontal table. The bead is made to describe horizontal circles on the table around the lower fixed point, with the string taut. What is the maximum value of ω, the angular speed of the bead, if it is to remain in contact with the table?

7 A fairground ride consists of a platform, which rotates horizontally. Ropes hang from the platform and people sit in cradles, suspended by the ropes. One rope is 5 m long and hangs from a point 5 m from the centre of rotation. A child sits in the cradle, which rotates in a horizontal circle. If the angle between the rope and the vertical is $\tan^{-1}\left(\frac{3}{4}\right)$ find the angular speed of the ride.

8 Two particles of mass *m* and 2*m* are connected by a light inextensible string which passes through a smooth fixed ring. The heavier particle hangs in equilibrium below the ring and the lighter particle describes a horizontal circle of radius *r*. Find the angular speed of the lighter particle in terms of *r* and *g*.

9 One end of a light inextensible string of length *l* is fixed at a point *A* and a particle *P* of mass *m* is attached to the other end. The particle moves in a horizontal circle with constant angular speed ω. Given that the centre of the circle is vertically below *A* and that the string remains taut with *AP* inclined at an angle α to the downward vertical, find $\cos \alpha$ in terms of *l*, *g* and ω.   [A]

10 A particle *P* is attached to one end of a light inextensible string of length 0.125 m, the other end of the string being attached to a fixed point, *O*. The particle describes, with constant speed, and with the string taut, a horizontal circle whose centre is vertically below *O*. Given that the particle describes exactly two complete revolutions per second find, in terms of *g* and π, the cosine of the angle between *OP* and the vertical.   [A]

11 A particle *P* of mass *m* moves in a horizontal circle, with uniform speed *v*, on the smooth inner surface of a fixed thin, hollow hemisphere of base radius *a*. The plane of motion of *P* is a distance $\frac{a}{4}$ below the horizontal plane, containing the rim of the hemisphere. Find, in terms of *m*, *g* and *a*, as appropriate, the speed *v* and the reaction of the surface on *P*.

A light inextensible string is now attached to *P*. The string passes through a small smooth hole at the lowest point of the hemisphere, and has a particle of mass *m* hanging at rest at the other end. Given that *P* now moves in a horizontal circle, on the inner surface of the hemisphere with uniform speed *u*, and that the plane of the motion is now distant $\frac{a}{2}$ below the horizontal plane of the rim, prove that:

$$u^2 = 3ga$$ [A]

12 The point *A* is vertically above point *B*, and a distance 5*a* from it. A particle *P* of mass *m* is attached to *A* by a light inextensible string of length 4*a*. The particle is also attached to *B* by a light inextensible string of length 3*a*. *P* moves in a horizontal circle with both strings taut. Find the tension in the strings and show that:

$$\omega^2 \geqslant \frac{5g}{16a}$$ [A]

13 A particle moves with constant speed *u* in a horizontal circle of radius *a* on the inside of a fixed smooth spherical shell of internal radius 2*a*. Show that $u^2\sqrt{3} = ag$.   [A]

14 An aeroplane of mass m kg describes a horizontal circle of radius r m at a constant speed of v m s^{-1}.

(a) Find the magnitude of the resultant force on the aeroplane if $m = 2000$, $v = 50$ and $r = 500$.

(b) A lift force of magnitude L N acts on the aeroplane. This force lies in the vertical plane that contains the aeroplane and the centre of the circle and acts at an angle α to the vertical when the aeroplane is flying in a circle at a constant speed. Find L and α in terms of v, r and g.

(c) Describe how L and α would change if the radius of the circle were reduced, but the speed of the aeroplane remained unchanged. [A]

15 A child of mass 40 kg swings on the end of a rope of length 4 m, moving in a horizontal circle at a constant speed. The rope is at angle of 30° to the vertical. The centre of the circle is at a height of 1.5 m above a point O on the ground. Model the child as a particle at the end of the rope.

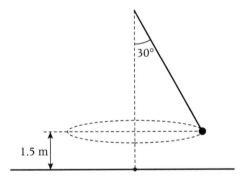

(a) Find
   (i) the tension in the rope
   (ii) the acceleration of the child
   (iii) her speed.

The child lets go of the rope and falls freely under gravity.

(b) Find the time that it takes for the child to reach the ground and state a reason why, in reality, this is an over-estimate.

(c) Find the maximum distance that the child could land from the point O. Draw a diagram to show the region in which the child could land and state the distance of the boundaries of this region from the point O. [A]

16 A conical pendulum consists of a string of length 0.5 m, with a particle of mass 3 kg attached at one end. The other end of the string is fixed to a point O. The particle describes a horizontal circle at constant speed. The centre of the circle is at the point Q, vertically below O. The string makes an angle of 30° with the vertical as shown in the diagram. Take $g = 10 \text{ m s}^{-2}$.

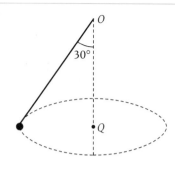

(a) State **two** assumptions that should be made about the string in order to form a simple model of the situation.

(b) (i) Show that the tension in the string is $20\sqrt{3}$ N.

   (ii) If ω radians per second is the angular speed of the particle, show that $\omega^2 = \dfrac{40\sqrt{3}}{3}$.

A second string, of the same length, is attached to the particle and to a point P, vertically below Q, such that $OQ = QP$, as shown in the diagram below. The particle describes the same circle as in part **(b)**, but at twice the angular speed.

(c) Find the tension in each string.   [A]

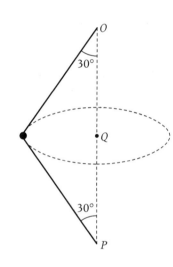

17 A particle, of mass m, is attached by a light, inextensible string, of length l, to the top of a smooth cone. The particle is set into motion so that it describes a horizontal circle on the outer surface of the cone as shown in the diagram below.

(a) Show that the tension in the string has magnitude $m\left(\dfrac{v^2}{l} + \dfrac{g}{\sqrt{2}}\right)$, when the particle describes a circle at a constant speed v.

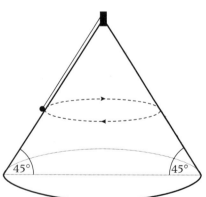

(b) Find the magnitude of the normal reaction force that the cone exerts on the particle.

(c) What will happen if $v^2 > \dfrac{gl}{\sqrt{2}}$? Justify your answer.   [A]

18 A fairground ride consists of a circular drum. The drum is a circular cylinder with vertical sides and of radius 2 m. It rotates about a vertical axis, and when it has reached its normal operating speed, the floor of the drum is removed so that the people on the ride move in a horizontal circle 'stuck' to the inside of the drum. At its normal operating speed, the drum completes 1 revolution every 2 seconds. Model a person on the ride as a particle.

(a) Find the acceleration of a person on the ride, at its normal operating speed.

(b) Draw and label a diagram to show the forces acting on a person on the ride, when the floor has been removed. Find the magnitude of the reaction and friction forces acting on a person of mass 70 kg in this situation.

(c) The operators propose a new design in which the sides of the drum are at angle θ to the horizontal as shown in the diagram below.

Assume that people on the ride still move in a circle of radius 2 m and at the same angular speed as before. Show that the magnitude of the friction force, F, acting on a person of mass m, is given by

$$F = mg \sin \theta - 2\pi^2 m \cos \theta.$$

Hence show that F is zero when $\tan \theta = \dfrac{2\pi^2}{g}$. [A]

19 The diagram shows a truncated cone. The radius of the cone decreases from 40 cm to 30 cm and the height of the truncated cone is 50 cm.

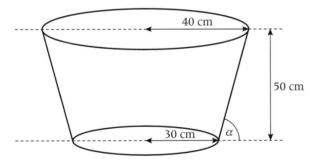

The angle between the sloping surface of the cone and the horizontal is α.

(a) Find $\tan \alpha$.

A coin is projected into the truncated cone, so that it rolls round on the inside surface.

When the coin is inside the truncated cone, it is modelled as a particle that **slides** on a smooth surface and it is assumed that there is no air resistance. The coin is assumed to move in a horizontal circle, on the inside surface of the coin, at a constant speed.

(b) Show that if the coin moves in a circle of radius r m, its speed, v m s^{-1}, is given by $v = \sqrt{rg \tan \alpha}$.

(c) Find the range of speeds for which the coin can be modelled as a particle describing a horizontal circle inside the truncated cone.

In reality the coin slows down, gradually moves down the cone, and eventually drops out of the bottom. Assume that the coin moves in a horizontal circle, of radius 40 cm, when it enters the truncated cone and that later it moves in a circle, of radius 30 cm, just before it leaves the cone. The mass of the coin is 10 grams.

(d) Find the total energy lost by the coin, as it moves from the top to the bottom of the truncated cone.

(e) State one aspect of the motion of the coin that has been ignored by the use of the particle model.   [A]

3.5 Motion of a vehicle on a banked track

In an earlier section the motion of a car as it turned a circle on a horizontal road was considered. You found that when a car turns such a corner, friction acts towards the centre of the circle and prevents sliding. Friction, of course, has a maximum value, so there is a maximum speed that the car can take the bend without sliding. If the road is banked, however, this maximum speed will increase because the normal reaction will also have a component towards the centre. To model this motion you will consider a particle on a rough inclined plane. It is possible that the frictional force, F, can act either up or down the plane. There are three important cases which need consideration.

(a) If the car were on the point of sliding up the incline, F, would act down the plane. Consider this when investigating the maximum speed that the car can take the bend.

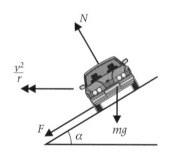

(b) If the car were on the point of sliding down the plane, F, would act up the plane. Consider this when investigating the minimum speed that the car can take the bend.

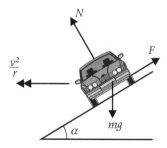

(c) Between the above two extremes, *F* can be zero. This is important for various reasons; reduced wear on tyres, greater comfort for passengers, and safety. There will be an optimum speed, which will ensure this.

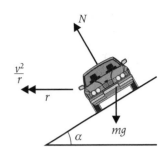

Worked example 3.9 _____

A car takes a bend on a racetrack, which is banked at 10° to the horizontal. The radius of the curve is 100 m, and the coefficient of friction between the tyres and road is 0.8. Find the greatest speed that the car can take the bend, if it travels in a horizontal circle.

Solution

The diagram shows the forces acting on the car.

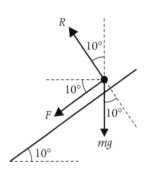

Using $F = ma$ radially gives

$$R \sin 10° + F \cos 10° = \frac{mv^2}{100} \tag{1}$$

Resolving vertically gives

$$R \cos 10° = mg + F \sin 10° \tag{2}$$
$$R \cos 10° - F \sin 10° = mg$$

When the speed is a maximum the car will be on the point of sliding, so friction will be limiting, hence $F = \mu R$. This can be used to substitute for *F* in the two equations above, which then become

$$R \sin 10° + 0.8\,R \cos 10° = \frac{mv^2}{100}$$

$$R \cos 10° - 0.8\,R \sin 10° = mg$$

If we now divide these two equations, then *R* will cancel on the left-hand side.

$$\frac{R \sin 10° + 0.8\,R \cos 10°}{R \cos 10° - 0.8\,R \sin 10°} = \frac{mv^2}{100mg}$$

$$\frac{\sin 10° + 0.8 \cos 10°}{\cos 10° - 0.8 \sin 10°} = \frac{v^2}{100g}$$

$$v^2 = 100g \left(\frac{\sin 10° + 0.8 \cos 10°}{\cos 10° - 0.8 \sin 10°} \right)$$

$$v = 33.4 \text{ m s}^{-1} \text{ (to 3 sf)}$$

Note: equations (1) and (2) are a pair of simultaneous equations for R and F, which can be solved to get the values of R and F.

$(1) \times \sin 10° + (2) \times \cos 10°$ gives

$$R(\sin^2 10° + \cos^2 10°) = \frac{mv^2 \sin 10°}{100} + mg \cos 10°$$

$$R = \frac{mv^2 \sin 10°}{100} + mg \cos 10°$$

Similarly $(1) \times \cos 10° - (2) \times \sin 10°$ gives

$$F(\sin^2 10° + \cos^2 10°) = \frac{mv^2 \cos 10°}{100} - mg \sin 10°$$

$$F = \frac{mv^2 \cos 10°}{100} - mg \sin 10°$$

Worked example 3.10

The radius of a bend in a road is r, and the road is banked at α to the horizontal. Find the speed at which a vehicle should take the bend, so that there is no tendency to slip.

Solution

The diagram shows the forces acting on the vehicle when it is modelled as a particle. Note that because there is no tendency to slip a friction force has not been included.

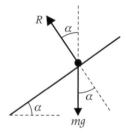

Using $F = ma$ radially gives

$$R \sin \alpha = \frac{mv^2}{r}$$

Resolving vertically

$$R \cos \alpha = mg$$

Dividing these two equations gives

$$\frac{\sin \alpha}{\cos \alpha} = \tan \alpha = \frac{v^2}{rg}$$

So, the optimum speed is given by

$$v^2 = rg \tan \alpha.$$

The vehicle in the previous example was not specified. The optimum speed found is particularly applicable to locomotives. When a train turns a corner on a piece of horizontal track, friction does not provide the horizontal force, but the rails do. This force can be very large, because of the large mass of the train. If a train needs to turn at high speeds, then it is necessary to bank the track, for safety.

Worked example 3.11

A vehicle, of mass 1 tonne, takes a bend of radius 50 m, on a horizontal road without slipping. The car travels at 25 m s⁻¹, and the road is banked at 15° to the horizontal. The car travels in a horizontal circle. Find the frictional force and the normal reaction of the road on the car. What is the minimum value of the coefficient of friction?

Solution

The diagram shows the forces acting on the vehicle, when it is modelled as a particle.

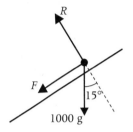

The first consideration is that we do not know whether the frictional force acts up or down the plane. However, this does not cause a problem. We can assume that it acts down the plane, and if we have chosen incorrectly our answer will turn out negative, but will still have the correct magnitude.

Using $F = ma$ radially gives

$$R \sin 15° + F \cos 15° = 1000 \times \frac{25^2}{50}$$
$$R \sin 15° + F \cos 15° = 12\,500 \qquad (1)$$

Resolving vertically gives

$$R \cos 15° = 1000\,g + F \sin 15°$$
$$R \cos 15° - F \sin 15° = 9800 \qquad (2)$$

To find R we calculate $(1) \times \sin 15° + (2) \times \cos 15°$ gives

$$R (\sin^2 15° + \cos^2 15°) = 12\,500 \sin 15° + 9800 \cos 15°$$
$$R = 12.7 \text{ kN}$$

Similarly $(1) \times \cos 15° - (2) \times \sin 15°$ gives

$$F (\sin^2 15° + \cos^2 15°) = 12\,500 \cos 15° - 9800 \sin 15°$$
$$F = 9.54 \text{ kN}$$

Using $F \leqslant \mu R$ gives

$$9.54 \leqslant 12.7\mu$$
$$\mu \geqslant 0.751$$

EXERCISE 3D

1 A car is negotiating a bend of radius 100 m, banked at an angle of 5°. What is the maximum speed at which it can do this, if the coefficient of friction is 1.0, the car does not slip, and the path of the car is in a horizontal plane?
  At what angle must the bend be banked if the car is to negotiate the bend without any tendency to slip at a speed of 80 km/h?

2 A stunt man is required to drive a car round a tightly banked corner, in a horizontal circle. The track is banked at 60° to the horizontal, and the radius of the bend is 30 m, and the coefficient of friction is 0.5. Find the minimum speed that he must drive if there is to be no slipping.

3 A train of mass 100 tonnes travels round a banked track, which forms part of a circle of radius 1250 m. The distance between the rail centres is 1.5 m and the outer rail is 37.5 mm vertically higher than the inner rail. If the train is travelling at 63 km/h, show that the sideways force on the rails is zero.

4 One lap of a circular cycle track is 400 m, and the track is banked at 45°. At what speed can the track be negotiated without any tendency to slip?

5 The radius of a bend on a horizontal piece of railway track is 750 m. The distance between the centres of the rails is 1.5 m. The average speed of trains on this stretch of track is 120 km/h. Find the height of the outer rail above the inner rail, if a train travelling at the average speed is to exert no sideways force on the rails.

6 A vehicle of mass 950 kg takes a bend of radius 60 m, without slipping. The speed of the vehicle is 20 m s^{-1}, and the road is banked at 20° to the horizontal. The vehicle travels in a horizontal circle. Find the frictional force and the normal reaction of the road on the vehicle. What is the least value of the coefficient of friction?

7 A car undergoing trials is moving on a horizontal surface around a circular bend of radius 50 m at a steady speed of 14 m s^{-1}. Calculate the least value of the coefficient of friction between the tyres of the car and the road surface.
Find the angle to the horizontal at which the bend should be banked in order that the car can move in a horizontal circle of radius 50 m at 14 m s^{-1} without any tendency to slip.
Another section of the test area is circular and banked at 30° to the horizontal. The coefficient of friction between the tyres of the car and the road surface is 0.6. Calculate the greatest speed at which the car can move in a horizontal of radius 70 m around the banked test area. [A]

8 A car, of mass 1200 kg, travels round a bend, of radius 50 m, at a constant speed of 20 m s^{-1}. Model the car as a particle and assume that there is no air resistance acting on it.

(a) A simple model assumes that the road is horizontal. Find the magnitude of the friction force acting on the car.

(b) In reality the road is banked at 2° to the horizontal. Find the magnitude of the friction force acting on the car.

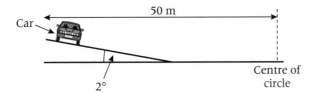

Draw and label a diagram to show the forces on the car and find a revised value for the magnitude of the friction force that takes account of the banking. [A]

3.6 Motions in a vertical circle at constant speed

In this chapter a simple case of vertical circular motion, in which the speed of the object moving in the circle remains constant will be considered. An example of this would be an item of clothing that moves in a vertical circle during the drying phase of a washing machine cycle.

Worked example 3.12

A jumper has a mass of 0.4 kg when wet. It is inside a washing machine drum that has a radius of 35 cm and rotates at 1200 rpm. Model the jumper as a particle that travels in a vertical circle. Find the magnitude of the reaction force on the jumper at its highest and lowest positions.

Solution

First we will convert the angular speed from rpm to rad s^{-1}.

$$\omega = \frac{1200 \times 2\pi}{60}$$

$$= 40\pi \text{ rad s}^{-1}$$

The diagram shows the forces acting on the jumper at its highest point. As both these forces act towards the centre of the circle we can apply $F = ma$ radially to give

$$R + 0.4 \times 9.8 = 0.4 \times 0.35 \times (40\pi)^2$$
$$R = 2207 \text{ N}$$

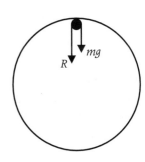

The second diagram shows the forces acting at the lowest point. In this case we can apply $F = ma$ radially to give

$$R - 0.4 \times 9.8 = 0.4 \times 0.35 \times (40\pi)^2$$
$$R = 2214\,\text{N}$$

We can see that the reaction force only varies by a very small amount between these two positions.

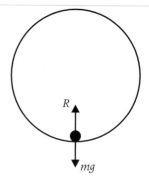

Worked example 3.13

A drum has a radius of 2 m. Initially the drum rotates around a vertical axis with people standing against the inside surface of the drum. When the drum reaches a certain speed it is moved so that it rotates around a horizontal axis with the people in it travelling in vertical circles. Find the minimum safe angular speed for the drum.

Solution

A force of magnitude $mr\omega^2$, must always act towards the centre of the circle. This force will be provided by the reaction force from the surface of the drum and the component of gravity acting towards the centre of the circle.

The diagram shows the forces acting in one position.

Apply $F = ma$ radially gives

$$R - mg\cos\theta = mr\omega^2$$
$$R = mr\omega^2 + mg\cos\theta$$

The person in the drum will complete vertical circle provided they remain in contact with the inside of the drum, that is if $R \geqslant 0$ for all values of θ.

$$mr\omega^2 + mg\cos\theta \geqslant 0$$
$$mr\omega^2 \geqslant -mg\cos\theta$$

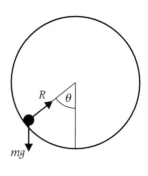

As this is true for all values of θ, we must take the minimum value of $\cos\theta$, which is -1 to give

$$mr\omega^2 \geqslant mg$$

$$\omega \geqslant \sqrt{\frac{g}{r}}$$

Substituting $r = 2$ gives

$$\omega \geqslant \sqrt{4.9} = 2.21\ \text{rad s}^{-1}$$

EXERCISE 3E

1 An item of clothing inside a washing machine is modelled as a particle, of mass 0.6 kg. The drum of the washing machine has radius 60 cm and rotates at 900 rpm. Assume that the clothing travels in a vertical circle at a constant speed.

Find the magnitude of the reaction force on the clothing, when it is

(a) at its highest point

(b) level with the centre of the drum

(c) at its lowest point.

2 In a film a stuntman, of mass 80 kg, holds onto the end of the sail of a windmill, so that he describes a vertical circle of radius 4 m, moving at a constant speed. Model the stuntman as a particle at the end of one of the sails. The sails complete one revolution every 10 seconds.

Find the magnitude of the force that the stuntman must exert at his lowest point.

3 A disc of radius 2.5 m rotates at 120 rpm about a horizontal axis. A small object, of mass 5 kg, is attached to the edge of the disc with Velcro, so that it describes a vertical circle.

(a) Find the maximum force that the Velcro must exert on the disc if the object is to travel in a circle at this speed.

(b) If the Velcro can only provide a force of magnitude 2000 N, describe the position of the object when it leaves contact with the disc.

4 An aeroplane of mass 3000 kg, that loops the loop is to be modelled as a particle that describes a circle of radius 200 m while travelling at a constant 60 m s^{-1}.

Assume that due to the wings a force, L N, acts on the plane and is always directed towards the centre of the circle.

Find L, when the plane is at each of the positions shown in the diagram, where OA is horizontal.

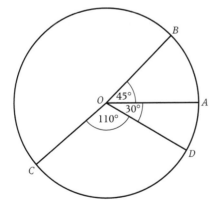

5 The wheel of a car has radius 30 cm. At the centre of the wheel is a hub cap of radius 15 cm. A stone is placed inside the hub cap, so that when the car goes fast enough the stone describes a vertical circle in contact with the inside surface of the hub cap. Find the minimum speed of the car for which the stone will remain in contact with the surface of the hub cap.

Key point summary

1 $1 \text{ rpm} = \dfrac{2\pi}{60} \text{ rad s}^{-1}$. *p61*

2 The velocity has magnitude $r\omega$ and is directed along a tangent to the circle. *p61*

3 It can be useful to express the magnitude of acceleration in terms of speed, v, rather than ω. *p62*

From $v = r\omega$, $\omega = \dfrac{v}{r}$ and by substituting this,

the expression for the magnitude of acceleration becomes

$$a = r\left(\frac{v}{r}\right)^2 = \frac{v^2}{r}.$$

4 When a particle moves in a horizontal circle with constant speed, there are two principles that can always be applied: *p64*

- resultant of vertical components of forces must be zero

- $F = ma$ can be applied radially.

Test yourself	What to review

1 A coin, of mass 20 g, is placed on a turntable that rotates at 50 rpm. The coefficient of friction between the coin and the turntable is 0.6.

Section 3.1

  (a) Find the maximum distance that the coin can be placed from the centre of the turntable if the coin is to travel in a circle.

  (b) Find the magnitude of the friction force in this case.

2 A ball, of mass 300 grams, is attached to one end of a light string of length 60 cm. The ball describes a horizontal circle with the string at an angle of 20° to the vertical.

Section 3.2

  (a) Find the speed of the ball.

  (b) Find the tension in the string.

3 A car travels in a horizontal circle of radius 75 m on a track that is banked at 5° to the horizontal. The coefficient of friction between the car and the track is 0.8.

Section 3.3

  (a) Find the speed at which the car has no tendency to slip.

  (b) Find the maximum speed of the car on the bend.

4 A small sphere, of mass 3 kg, is attached to the end of a light rod of length 1.5 m. The rod rotates at 90 rpm. Find the tension in the rod when it is:

Section 3.4

  (a) horizontal

  (b) vertical, with the sphere above the centre of the circle

  (c) at an angle of 45° to the vertical with the sphere higher than the centre of the circle.

3

Test yourself **ANSWERS**

1 (a) 21.4 cm   **(b)** 0.118 N.

2 (a) 0.856 m s^{-1} **(b)** 3.13 N.

3 (a) 8.02 m s^{-1} **(b)** 26.5 m s^{-1}.

4 (a) 400 N   **(b)** 370 N   **(c)** 379 N.

CHAPTER 4

Centres of mass by integration

Learning objectives

After studying this chapter you should be able to:

- use strips to find the centre of mass of a uniform lamina
- use discs to find the centre of mass of a solid formed by rotating a region through 360° around the x-axis
- use rings to find the centre of mass of a shell formed by rotating a line around the x-axis
- know that when a body is suspended in equilibrium, the centre of mass will be directly below the point of suspension
- know that when a body is on the point of toppling on an inclined plane the centre of mass must be directly above the point about which the body will topple.

4.1 Introduction

In the M1 module you will have considered the centre of mass of a system of particles and of a composite body. These ideas will be reviewed briefly at the start of this chapter and then you will move on to consider the centre of mass of any shaped lamina and then for solids and shells formed by rotating a region or line about the x-axis.

4.2 Laminae

Consider a set of particles $m_1, m_2, \ldots, m_n$, which are fixed at points (x_1, y_1), $(x_2, y_2) \ldots, (x_n, y_n)$. The centre of mass of the particles is at a point $(\bar{x}, \bar{y})$ through which the combined weight will act.

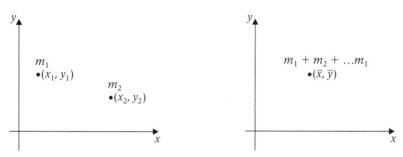

Taking moments about the y-axis we get

$$m_1x_1 + m_2x_2 + \ldots, m_nx_n = (m_1 + m_2 + \ldots mn)\bar{x}$$

Using the Σ notation we can rewrite this result as

$$\bar{x}\sum_{i=1}^{n} m_i = \sum_{i=1}^{n} m_i x_i$$

By taking moments about the x-axis, we can similarly obtain

$$\bar{y}\sum_{i=1}^{n} m_i = \sum_{i=1}^{n} m_i y_i$$

> The lamina equations are used to find the centre of mass of a system of particles. They can also be used to find the centre of mass of a composite lamina, that is a lamina, which can be divided into separate shapes, the centres of mass of which must be known.

Worked example 4.1

A uniform lamina *ABCDE* consists of a rectangle *ABDE*, 8 cm × 10 cm, and an isosceles triangle *BCD*, where *BC* = *DC* = 5 cm, as shown. Find the distance of the centre of mass of the lamina from *AE*.

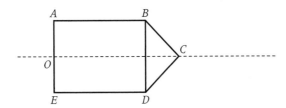

Solution

The lamina has a line of symmetry through *C*, parallel to *AB*, and so its centre of mass will lie along this line. Let the origin, *O*, be the mid-point of *AE*, and *OC* be the *x*-axis. The lamina can be divided into two separate parts. The masses and positions of their centres of mass can be determined.

Let the density of the lamina be ρ (i.e. let the mass of 1 cm² of the lamina be ρ kg).

The mass of the rectangle is given by

$$\text{mass} = \text{area} \times \text{density}$$
$$= 80\rho.$$

The centre of mass of the rectangle is at (5,0).

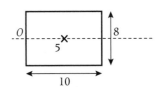

The mass of the triangle is given by

$$\text{mass} = \text{area} \times \text{density}$$
$$= 12\rho.$$

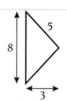

The centre of mass of the triangle is at $(11,0)$.

(The centre of mass of a triangle lies one-third of the way along the median from the base.)

It is helpful to arrange these results in a table.

Body	Mass	x-coordinate
Whole lamina	92ρ	$\bar{x}$
Rectangle	80ρ	5
Triangle	12ρ	11

Taking moments about AE now gives

$$92\rho\bar{x} = 80\rho \times 5 + 12\rho \times 11$$
$$= 532\rho$$
$$\bar{x} = 5.78.$$

Examples like this one have been seen before in the previous module. However, this technique can also used when you can divide the lamina into an infinite number of small strips and sum the separate moments using integration. Consider a uniform lamina defined by the area bounded by

- the curve $y = f(x)$
- the x-axis
- the line $x = a$
- the line $x = b$.

The diagram shows the lamina and a strip of width δx. It is by considering the whole lamina as a composite body made up of many of these strips that the position of the centre of mass can be found.

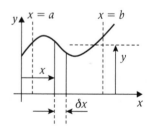

Let the density of the lamina be ρ. The mass of the lamina is given by

$$\text{mass} = \text{density} \times \text{area}$$
$$= \rho \int_a^b y \, dx$$

The lamina can be divided into thin strips of width δx. The mass of each strip is given by

$$\text{mass} = \text{density} \times \text{area}$$
$$= \rho y \delta x$$

As the strip is very thin, the coordinates of the centre of mass of

the strip are approximately $\left(x, \dfrac{y}{2}\right)$.

The following table summarises these results.

Body	Mass	x-coordinate	y-coordinate
Whole lamina	$\rho\displaystyle\int_a^b ydx$	$\bar{x}$	$\bar{y}$
Strips	$\rho y\delta x$	x	$\dfrac{y}{2}$

Taking moments about the y-axis and summing all the contributions from the strips you have

$$\bar{x}\rho\int_a^b ydx = \sum_{x=a}^{x=b} \rho xy\delta x.$$

As $\delta x \to 0$, this equation becomes

$$\bar{x}\int_a^b ydx = \int_a^b xydx$$

which gives the general result

$$\bar{x} = \frac{\displaystyle\int_a^b xydx}{\displaystyle\int_a^b ydx} \quad \text{or} \quad \bar{x} = \frac{1}{\text{area}} \times \int_a^b xydx$$

You can find the y-coordinate of the centre of mass by taking moments about the x-axis and summing the contributions of the strips.

$$\bar{y}\int_a^b ydx = \sum_{x=a}^{x=b} \frac{y}{2} \times \rho ydx$$

As $\delta x \to 0$, this equation becomes

$$\bar{y}\int_a^b ydx = \int_a^b \frac{1}{2} y^2 dx$$

which leads to the general result

$$\bar{y} = \frac{\displaystyle\int_a^b \frac{1}{2} y^2 dx}{\displaystyle\int_a^b ydx} \quad \text{or} \quad \bar{y} = \frac{1}{\text{area}} \times \int_a^b \frac{1}{2} y^2 dx$$

Worked example 4.2

Find the coordinates of the centre of mass of the uniform lamina bounded by the curve $y = x^2$, the x-axis, and the line $x = 2$.

Solution

The diagram shows the lamina under consideration.

First find the area of the lamina.

$$\text{Area} = \int_0^2 y\,dx = \int_0^2 x^2\,dx = \left[\frac{1}{3}x^3\right]_0^2 = \frac{8}{3}$$

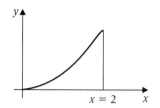

Then use

$$\bar{x} = \frac{1}{\text{area}} \times \int_a^b xy\,dx \text{ to find } \bar{x}.$$

$$\bar{x} = \frac{3}{8} \times \int_0^2 xy\,dx$$

$$= \frac{3}{8} \times \int_0^2 x^3\,dx$$

$$= \frac{3}{8}\left[\frac{x^4}{4}\right]_0^2$$

$$= 1.5$$

Then use

$$\bar{y} = \frac{1}{\text{area}} \times \int_a^b \frac{1}{2}y^2\,dx \text{ to find } \bar{y}.$$

$$\bar{y} = \frac{3}{8} \times \int_0^2 \frac{1}{2}y^2\,dx$$

$$= \frac{3}{8} \times \int_0^2 \frac{1}{2}x^4\,dx$$

$$= \frac{3}{8}\left[\frac{x^5}{10}\right]_0^2$$

$$= 1.2$$

The centre of mass of the lamina is at (1.5,1.2).

Equilibrium of suspended bodies

If a rigid body is in equilibrium the resultant force on the body must be zero. In particular, if only two forces are acting on the body, they must be equal and opposite, and act along the same line.

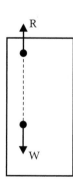

> When a rigid body is freely suspended from a fixed point the centre of mass of the body must be vertically below the point of suspension.

This principle which you will have used in the M1 module will be applied in the next example.

Worked example 4.3

A uniform triangular lamina, *ABC*, is bounded by the lines

- $y = 3x$
- $x = h$.

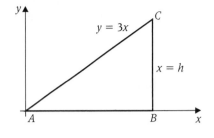

(a) Show that the coordinates of its centre of mass are

$$\left(\frac{2}{3}h, h\right).$$

(b) The lamina is suspended from the corner *A*.

Find the angle between the side *AB* and the vertical.

4

Solution

(a) First find the area of the lamina.

$$\text{Area} = \frac{1}{2} \times h \times 3h = \frac{3}{2}h^2$$

Then use

$$\bar{x} = \frac{1}{\text{area}} \times \int_a^b xy\,dx \text{ to find } \bar{x}.$$

$$\bar{x} = \frac{2}{3h^2} \times \int_0^h xy\,dx$$

$$= \frac{2}{3h^2} \times \int_0^h 3x^2\,dx$$

$$= \frac{2}{3h^2}\left[x^3\right]_0^h$$

$$= \frac{2}{3}h$$

Then use

$$\bar{y} = \frac{1}{\text{area}} \times \int_a^b \frac{1}{2}y^2\,dx \text{ to find } \bar{y}.$$

$$\bar{y} = \frac{2}{3h^2} \times \int_0^h y^2\,dx$$

$$= \frac{2}{3h^2} \times \int_0^h \frac{9}{2}x^2\,dx$$

$$= \frac{2}{3h^2}\left[\frac{3x^3}{2}\right]_0^h$$

$$= h$$

So the coordinates of its centre of mass are $\left(\frac{2}{3}h, h\right)$.

(b) When the lamina is suspended from the corner A, it will hang with the centre of mass, G, directly below A. This situation is shown in the diagram opposite.

The angle between AB and the vertical has been labelled α on the diagram opposite.

To find α note that $AD = \dfrac{2h}{3}$ and that $DG = h$.

$$\tan \alpha = \frac{DG}{AD}$$
$$= h \times \frac{3}{2h}$$
$$= \frac{3}{2}$$
$$\alpha = 56.3°$$

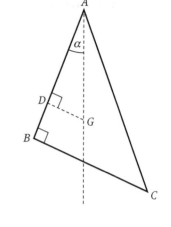

The formulae used above are very useful in examples like the previous one. However, they cannot be relied upon entirely. The whole method from first principles could be asked for in an examination. Furthermore, these formulae do not apply to some laminas. The next worked example considers a lamina that is not bounded by the x-axis.

Worked example 4.4

Find the coordinates of the centre of mass of the uniform lamina, which is bounded by the curves,

(a) $y = x^2 - 4x + 7$,

(b) $y = 8x - 3 - x^2$.

Solution

First, find where these curves intersect. This will be where

$$x^2 - 4x + 7 = 8x - 3 - x^2$$
$$2x^2 - 12x + 10 = 0$$
$$2(x - 1)(x - 5) = 0$$
$$x = 1 \text{ or } 5.$$

A sketch of the lamina is shown below.

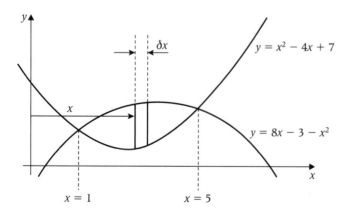

The area of the lamina is

$$\int_1^5 [(8x - 3 - x^2) - (x^2 - 4x + 7)]dx = \int_1^5 (12x - 2x^2 - 10)dx$$

$$= \left[6x^2 - \frac{2}{3}x^3 - 10x \right]_1^5 = \frac{64}{3}$$

If the density of the lamina is ρ, then the area of it is $\frac{64}{3}\rho$.

The lamina can be divided into a large number of thin vertical strips of width δx. The area of a typical strip is

$$[(8x - x^2 - 3) - (x^2 - 4x + 7)]\delta x = (12x - 2x^2 - 10)\delta x$$

The mass of the strip is $(12x - 2x^2 - 10)\delta x \rho$.

The centre of mass of the strip will be at the mid-point of $(x, x^2 - 4x + 7)$ and $(x, 8x - x^2 - 3)$, which is $(x, 2x + 2)$.

Body	Mass	x-coordinate	y-coordinate
Whole lamina	$\frac{64}{3}\rho$	$\bar{x}$	$\bar{y}$
Strips	$(12x - 2x^2 - 10)\delta x \rho$	x	$2x + 2$

Taking moments about the y-axis and summing from $x = 1$ to $x = 5$

$$\frac{64}{3}\rho \bar{x} = \sum_{x=1}^{x=5} x(12x - 2x^2 - 10)\rho \delta x$$

As $\delta x \to 0$ this becomes

$$\frac{64}{3}\bar{x} = \int_1^5 (-2x^3 + 12x^2 - 10x)dx$$

$$= \left[-\frac{1}{2}x^4 + 4x^3 - 5x^2 \right]_1^5$$

$$= 64$$

Hence $\bar{x} = 3$.

Taking moments about the x-axis and summing from $x = 1$ to $x = 5$

$$\frac{64}{3}\bar{y} = \sum_{x=1}^{x=5} (2x + 2)(12x - 2x^2 - 10)\rho \delta x$$

As $\delta x \to 0$

$$\frac{64}{3}\bar{y} = \int_1^5 (-4x^3 + 20x^2 + 4x - 20)dx$$

$$= \left[-x^4 + \frac{20}{3}x^3 + 2x^2 - 20x \right]_1^5$$

$$= \frac{512}{3}$$

Hence

$$\frac{64}{3}\bar{y} = \frac{512}{3}$$

$$\bar{y} = \frac{512}{64} = 8$$

EXERCISE 4A

1 A uniform lamina is bounded by the lines and curves listed below. For each lamina find the coordinates of its centre of mass.

   (a) $y = x$, $y = 0$ and $x = 12$.

   (b) $y = x^2$, $y = 0$ and $x = 10$.

   (c) $y = 1 - x^2$ and $y = 0$.

   (d) $y = 9 - x^2$ and $y = 0$.

   (e) $y = 16 - x$, $y = 0$ and $x = 1$.

2 A uniform lamina is bounded by the x-axis, the y-axis and the curve $y = 8 - x^3$.

   (a) Find the coordinates of the centre of mass of the lamina.

   (b) The lamina is suspended from the right angled corner. Find the angle between the lamina's longest side and the vertical.

3 A uniform lamina consists of the finite region is bounded by the curve $y = 1 - x^4$ and the x-axis.

   (a) Find the area of the lamina.

   (b) Explain why the x-coordinate of the centre of mass of the lamina is 0.

   (c) Find the y-coordinate of the centre of mass of the lamina.

   (d) The lamina is suspended from one end of its straight edge. Find the angle between the straight edge and the horizontal.

4 Show that the centre of mass of a semi-circular, uniform lamina of radius a is at a distance $\dfrac{4a}{3\pi}$, from the base of the semicircle.

5 Find the coordinates of the centre of mass of the uniform lamina enclosed by these lines and curves.
$$y = 0, \ x = 0 \text{ and } y = \cos x, \text{ for } 0 \leqslant x \leqslant \frac{\pi}{2}.$$

6 A uniform lamina is bounded by the x axis and the curve $y = \sin x$ for $0 \leqslant x \leqslant \pi$. Find the angle between the straight edge of the lamina and the horizontal when it is suspended from one end of the straight edge.

7 A uniform lamina is in the shape of the finite region enclosed by the curve $y = x^2 + 1$ and the line $y = 10$. The lamina is suspended from the point which has cooordinates (2, 10). Find the angle between the straight edge of the lamina and the vertical.

8 A uniform lamina is in the shape of the triangular region which has corners at the points A, B and C which have coordinates (2,3), (8,9) and (8,0), respectively.

(a) Use integration to find the coordinates of the centre of mass of the lamina.

(b) The lamina is suspended from a point on the side AB so that the side BC is vertical. Find the coordinates of the point of suspension.

9 Find the coordinates of the centre of mass of the uniform lamina enclosed by the curves $y = 3 + x - x^2$ and $y = 3 - 3x + x^2$.

4.3 Volumes of revolution

There are several commonly occurring bodies, which are formed by revolving a region about a line. The most obvious examples are the cone (formed by rotating a triangle) and a hemisphere, or any part of a sphere between two parallel plane sections (formed by rotating a section of a circle).

The diagram shows a uniform solid of revolution, obtained by revolving the region bounded by the curve $y = f(x)$, and the lines $x = a$, $x = b$ and $y = 0$, about the x-axis.

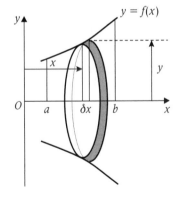

The volume of revolution can be divided into a large number of thin discs of thickness δx.

Let the density of the solid be ρ. The mass of the whole solid is:

$$\text{mass} = \text{density} \times \text{volume}$$

$$= \rho \times \int_a^b \pi y^2 dx$$

The mass of the typical disc is:

$$\text{mass} = \text{density} \times \text{volume}$$

$$= \rho \times \pi y^2 \delta x$$

Body	Mass	x-coordinate
Whole solid	$\rho \int_a^b \pi y^2 dx$	$\bar{x}$
Discs	$\rho \pi y^2 \delta x$	x

Taking moments about the *y*-axis and summing from $x = a$ to $x = b$

$$\bar{x}\rho \int_a^b \pi y^2 dx = \sum_{x=a}^{x=b} x\rho \pi y^2 dx$$

As $\delta x \rightarrow 0$, you will obtain the result

$$\bar{x} = \frac{\displaystyle\int_a^b xy^2 dx}{\displaystyle\int_a^b y^2 dx}$$

> The centre of mass of any solid that is formed by rotating a region through 360° around the *x*-axis can be found by using the volume of revolution formulae.

Worked example 4.5

Find the centre of mass of the uniform solid, formed by rotating the region bounded by the following curve and lines, through 360° about the *x*-axis.

$$y = \frac{8}{x^2}, y = 0, x = 2 \text{ and } x = 4.$$

Solution

The region that is to be rotated is shown in the diagram.

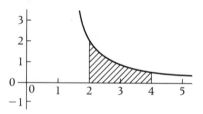

Use of the result $\bar{x} = \dfrac{\displaystyle\int_a^b xy^2 dx}{\displaystyle\int_a^b y^2 dx}$ gives

$$\bar{x} = \frac{\displaystyle\int_2^4 x\left(\frac{8}{x^2}\right)^2 dx}{\displaystyle\int_2^4 \left(\frac{8}{x^2}\right)^2 dx} = \frac{\displaystyle\int_2^4 \frac{64}{x^3}dx}{\displaystyle\int_2^4 \frac{64}{x^4}dx} = \frac{\left[-\dfrac{32}{x^2}\right]_2^4}{\left[-\dfrac{64}{3x^3}\right]_2^4} = \frac{6}{\frac{7}{3}} = \frac{18}{7}$$

Toppling of a rigid body on a rough inclined plane

If a rigid body rests in equilibrium on a rough inclined plane, then a vertical through its centre of mass, *G*, must cut the plane where the body is in contact with the plane, as shown in the diagram.

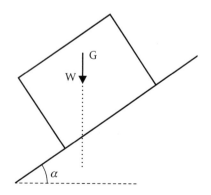

When the vertical through the centre of mass falls outside the region of contact between the body and plane then the body cannot rest in equilibrium: it will topple.

The greatest value of α for which equilibrium is possible
will be when the centre of mass is vertically above the end
point of contact, as shown below.

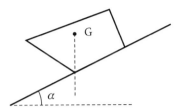

Worked example 4.6

4

(a) Show, from first principles, that the centre of mass of a
uniform hemisphere, of radius a, is at a distance $\dfrac{3a}{8}$ from its
base.

(b) The hemisphere is placed on a rough inclined plane. Find
the angle that the plane makes with the horizontal when
the hemisphere is on the point of toppling. Assume that the
hemisphere does not slide.

Solution

(a) The equation of a circle, of radius a, whose centre is the
origin is $x^2 + y^2 = a^2$. If the region in the first quadrant (as
shaded below) is rotated 360° about the x-axis, then a
hemisphere is described.

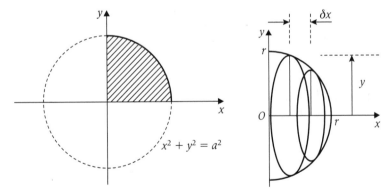

The hemisphere can be divided into a large number of thin
vertical discs of radius y and thickness δx.

Let the density of the solid be ρ. The mass of the solid will be

$$\text{mass} = \text{density} \times \text{volume}$$

$$= \rho \times \frac{1}{2} \times \frac{4\pi a^3}{3} = \frac{2}{3}\pi a^3 \rho$$

The mass of the thin disc is $\rho \pi y^2 \delta x$.

Body	Mass	x-coordinate
Hemisphere	$\frac{2}{3}\pi\rho a^3$	$\bar{x}$
Discs	$\rho\pi y^2\delta x$	x

Taking moments about the y-axis and summing from $x = 0$ to $x = a$,

$$\bar{x}\frac{2}{3}\pi\rho a^3 = \sum_{x=0}^{x=a} x\rho\pi y^2 \delta x$$

As $\delta x \to 0$

$$\bar{x} = \frac{3}{2a^3}\int_0^a x(a^2 - x^2)dx = \frac{3}{2a^3}\left[\frac{a^2 x^2}{2} - \frac{x^4}{4}\right]_0^a = \frac{3}{2a^3} \times \frac{a^4}{4} = \frac{3a}{8}$$

(b) The diagram shows the hemisphere placed on an inclined plane with the centre of mass, G, directly above the corner A. The midpoint of the diameter is the point B.

From the triangle that we obtain

$$\tan \alpha = \frac{AB}{BG} = \frac{a}{\frac{3a}{8}} = \frac{8}{3}$$

$$\alpha = 69.4°$$

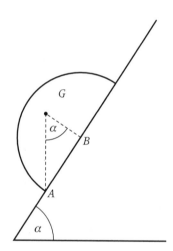

Worked example 4.7

A right, uniform, solid cone, of height h and base radius r, is formed by rotating the region defined below around the x-axis, through $360°$.

$$0 \leqslant y \leqslant \frac{rx}{h}, \quad \text{and} \quad 0 \leqslant x \leqslant h$$

(a) Show that
  (i) the volume of the cone is $\frac{1}{3}\pi r^2 h$
  (ii) the x-coordinate of the centre of mass is $\frac{3h}{4}$

(b) For a particular cone $r = \frac{h}{2}$. This cone is suspended from a point on the edge of its base. Find the angle between the base and the vertical when the cone is in equilibrium.

Solution

(a) (i) The volume will be given by $\pi \int_0^h y^2 dx$, which is evaluated below

$$V = \pi \int_0^h y^2 dx = \pi \int_0^h \frac{r^2}{h^2} x^2 dx = \pi \left[\frac{r^2 x^3}{3h^2} \right]_0^h = \frac{1}{3} \pi r^2 h$$

(ii) We can use the result $\bar{x} = \dfrac{\displaystyle\int_a^b xy^2 dx}{\displaystyle\int_a^b y^2 dx}$, with $a = 0, b = h$

and noting that we have already found the denominator in part **(i)**, to give

$$\bar{x} = \frac{\displaystyle\int_0^h \pi y^2 x dx}{\frac{1}{3} \pi r^2 h} = \frac{3}{r^2 h} \int_0^h \frac{r^2}{h^2} x^3 dx = \frac{3}{h^3} \times \left[\frac{x^4}{4} \right]_0^h = \frac{3}{h^3} \times \frac{h^4}{4} = \frac{3h}{4}$$

(b) The diagram shows the cross-section of the cone when it has been suspended. Note that in equilibrium, the centre of mass, G, will be directly below the point A from which the cone is suspended. The point B is at the centre of the base of the cone.

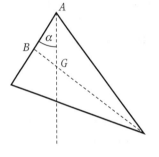

Using trigonometry gives

$$\tan \alpha = \frac{BG}{AB}$$
$$= \frac{\frac{h}{4}}{\frac{h}{2}}$$
$$= \frac{1}{2}$$
$$\alpha = 26.6°$$

EXERCISE 4B

1 The regions bounded by the curves and lines below are rotated through 360° about the x-axis to form uniform solids. In each case find the coordinates of the centre of mass.

(a) $y = x^3, x = 1$ and $y = 0$.

(b) $y = \dfrac{1}{x}, x = 1, x = 2$ and $y = 0$.

(c) $y = 1 + x, x = 2, x = 4$ and $y = 0$.

(d) $y = e^x, x = 0, x = 2$ and $y = 0$.

2 A uniform, solid cone is formed by rotating the region enclosed by the lines $y = \dfrac{x}{2}$, $y = 0$ and $x = 6$, through $360°$ around the x-axis.

   (a) Find the volume of the cone.

   (b) Find the distance of the centre of mass from the y-axis.

   (c) The cone is placed on an inclined plane with its flat surface in contact with the plane. Find the angle between the plane and the horizontal when the cone is on the point of toppling. Assume that the cone does not slide down the slope.

3 A solid is formed by rotating the region enclosed by the curve $y = \dfrac{1}{x}$ and the lines $x = 1$, $x = 4$ and $y = 0$ through $360°$ about the axis.

   (a) Show that the volume of the solid is $\dfrac{3\pi}{4}$.

   (b) Show that the centre of mass of the solid is at a distance $\dfrac{8\ln 2 - 3}{3}$ from the larger face of the solid.   [A]

4 A uniform solid is formed by rotating the region enclosed by the lines $y = x + 1$, $y = 0$ and $x = 4$ through $360°$ about the x-axis.

   (a) Find the distance of the centre of mass from the y-axis.

   (b) The solid is placed on an inclined plane with its larger flat face in contact with the plane. Find the angle between the plane and the horizontal when the solid is on the point of toppling. Assume that the solid does not slide.

   (c) Repeat **(b)**, but with the smaller face of the solid in contact with the plane.

5 The region enclosed by the curve $y = 4 - (x - 2)^2$ and the x-axis is rotated through $360°$ around the x-axis to form a uniform solid.

   (a) Use integration to show that the centre of mass is 2 units from the y-axis.

   (b) Sketch a graph of the region and explain how you could have obtained the result above without using integration.

6 The region enclosed by the curve $y = x + \dfrac{1}{x}$ and the lines $x = \dfrac{1}{2}$, $x = 3$ and $y = 0$ is rotated through $360°$ about the x-axis.

    (a) Find the distance of the centre of mass from the y-axis.

    (b) The solid is then suspended from a point on the edge of its larger flat face. Find the angle between this face and the vertical when the solid is in equilibrium.

7 Show by integration that the centre of mass of a uniform solid hemisphere, of base radius a, is at a distance $\dfrac{3a}{8}$ from the centre of its plane face.

    A uniform composite body consists of a uniform circular cylinder of radius a, and height a, and a uniform solid hemisphere of radius a, such that the plane face of the hemisphere coincides with the base of the cylinder. Determine the distance of the centre of mass of the composite body from the plane face of the hemisphere.   **[A]**

8 A uniform solid hemisphere, of radius a, is cut into two parts by a plane parallel to the plane face of the hemisphere and at a distance $\frac{1}{2}a$ from it. Find the volume of each of the two parts and the position of the centre of mass of each of the two parts.   **[A]**

9 A sphere, of radius a, is cut, by a plane, so that it produces the cross-section shown in the diagram. Consider the larger part of the sphere.

    (a) Calculate the distance of the centre of mass from the flat surface.

    (b) The solid is placed on an inclined plane with the flat surface in contact with the plane. Find the angle between the plane and the horizontal when the solid is on the point of toppling.

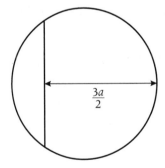

10 The region enclosed by the curve $y = \dfrac{1}{\sqrt{x}}$, the lines $x = 1$, $x = 4$ and the x-axis rotated through $360°$ around the x-axis to form a solid. Find the distance of the centre of mass of the solid from the y-axis.

4.4 Surface of revolution

When a curve $y = f(x)$ is rotated around the x-axis, it describes a surface. Here you will see how the centre of mass of such a body can be found in some special cases.

Worked example 4.8 (conical shell)

The surface of a uniform right circular cone, of height h and base radius r, can be generated by revolving the line $y = \dfrac{r}{h}x$ completely around the x-axis, between $x = 0$ to $x = h$. Prove by integration that the centre of mass lies at $(\frac{2}{3}h, 0)$.

Solution

The diagram shows the surface under consideration.

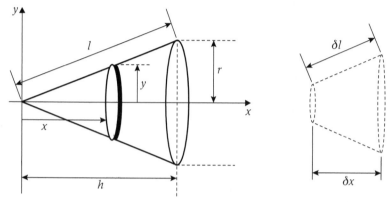

The cone can be divided into a series of thin rings, of thickness δx. An exaggerated version of a typical ring is also shown. The curved surface area (and so the mass also) of the cone depends upon the slant height l. The surface area of the ring will also, therefore, depend upon the slant height δl.

Let the slant height of the cone be l. From Pythagoras' theorem

$$l = \sqrt{r^2 + h^2}$$

(The formula for the curved surface area of a cone is $A = \pi r l$. However, we will prove this using integration.)

Using similar triangles

$$\frac{h}{l} = \frac{\delta x}{\delta l} \Rightarrow \delta l = \frac{l}{h}\delta x$$

The curved surface area of the ring is therefore $2\pi y \delta l$.

If the density of the body is ρ, then the mass of the ring is

$$2\pi y \rho \delta l = \frac{2\pi y \rho l}{h}\delta x = \frac{2\pi r l \rho x}{h^2}\delta x$$

The mass of the whole conical shell is approximately

$$M = \sum_{x=0}^{x=h} \frac{2\pi y \rho l}{h}\delta x = \sum_{x=0}^{x=h} \frac{2\pi r \rho l x}{h^2}\delta x.$$

As $\delta x \to 0$, we obtain the mass of the conical shell.

$$M = \frac{2\pi r \rho l}{h^2}\int_0^h x\,dx = \frac{2\pi r \rho l}{h^2} \times \frac{h^2}{2} = \pi r l \rho.$$

Body	Mass	x-coordinate
Cone	$\pi r l \rho$	$\bar{x}$
Rings	$\dfrac{2\pi r \rho l x}{h^2}\delta x$	x

Taking moments about the y-axis and summing from $x = 0$ to $x = h$

$$\pi r l \rho \bar{x} = \sum_{x=0}^{x=h} \frac{2\pi r \rho l x^2}{h^2}\,\delta x$$

As $\delta x \to 0$

$$\bar{x} = \frac{2}{h^2}\int_0^h x^2 dx = \frac{2}{h^2} = \frac{h^3}{3} = \frac{2h}{3}$$

Worked example 4.9

The line $y = x + 1$ for $0 \leqslant x \leqslant 6$ is rotated through $360°$ around the x-axis to form a hollow frustrum. Find the distance of the centre of mass of the frustrum from the y-axis.

Solution

The diagram shows the frustrum and a ring within it.

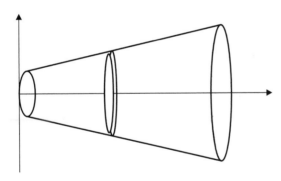

The mass of one ring will be $\rho \times 2\pi y \times \delta l$. To be able to proceed we need to find a relationship between δx *and* δl. The diagram shows the line and the small piece of it that forms the ring.

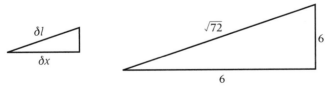

By comparing the triangles

$$\frac{\delta l}{\delta x} = \frac{\sqrt{72}}{6} = \sqrt{2}$$

$$\delta l = \sqrt{2}\,\delta x$$

Now we can obtain the mass of the frustum as

$$\text{mass} = \int_0^6 \rho 2\pi(x+1)\sqrt{2}\,dx$$

$$= 2\rho\pi\sqrt{2}\int_0^6 (x+1)\,dx$$

$$= 2\rho\pi\sqrt{2}\left[\frac{x^2}{2}+x\right]_0^6$$

$$= \rho\pi 48\sqrt{2}$$

Taking moments about the y-axis for the ring gives
$x \times \rho \times 2\pi y \times \delta l = \rho\pi 2\sqrt{2}xy\delta x$. Summing and letting $\delta x \to 0$ gives

$$\rho\pi 48\sqrt{2} \times \bar{x} = \int_0^6 \rho\pi 2\sqrt{2}x(x+1)\,dx$$

$$24\bar{x} = \int_0^6 (x^2+x)\,dx$$

$$\bar{x} = \frac{1}{24}\left[\frac{x^3}{3}+\frac{x^2}{2}\right]_0^6$$

$$= \frac{90}{24}$$

$$= 3.75$$

General results for straight lines

In the examples above we have had to consider the relationship between δx and δl. We can deduce a general relationship that will make it easier to solve problems.

Consider the triangle shown in the diagram which relates δx, δy and δl. By Pythagoras' theorem

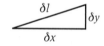

$$\delta l^2 = \delta x^2 + \delta y^2$$

Dividing through by δx^2 then gives

$$\left(\frac{\delta l}{\delta x}\right)^2 = 1 + \left(\frac{\delta y}{\delta x}\right)^2$$

But for a straight line $\dfrac{\delta y}{\delta x} = m$, where m is the gradient. Hence we have

$$\left(\frac{\delta l}{\delta x}\right)^2 = 1 + m^2$$

$$\delta l = \sqrt{1+m^2}\,\delta x$$

The mass of one ring will then be $2\rho\pi y\sqrt{1+m^2}\,\delta x$ and the total mass will be $2\rho\pi\int_a^b y\sqrt{1+m^2}\,dx$

The moment of one ring will then be $2\rho\pi xy\sqrt{1+m^2}\,\delta x$ and the total moment will be $2\rho\pi\int_a^b xy\sqrt{1+m^2}\,dx$

The general result given can be deduced from this and is given below.

$$\bar{x} = \frac{\displaystyle\int_a^b xy\sqrt{1 + m^2}\,dx}{\displaystyle\int_a^b y\sqrt{1 + m^2}\,dx} = \frac{\displaystyle\int_a^b xy\,dx}{\displaystyle\int_a^b y\,dx}$$

This result is now applied in the following example.

Worked example 4.10

The line $y = 8 - 2x$ is rotated through $360°$ around the x-axis for $0 \leqslant x \leqslant 4$ to form a conical shell. Find the distance of the centre of mass from the x-axis.

Solution

Using the result $\bar{x} = \dfrac{\displaystyle\int_a^b xy\,dx}{\displaystyle\int_a^b y\,dx}$ gives,

$$\bar{x} = \frac{\displaystyle\int_0^4 x(8 - 2x)\,dx}{\displaystyle\int_0^4 (8 - 2x)\,dx}$$

$$= \frac{\left[4x^2 - \dfrac{2x^3}{3}\right]_0^4}{\left[8x - x^2\right]_0^4}$$

$$= \frac{\frac{64}{3}}{16}$$

$$= \frac{4}{3}$$

EXERCISE 4C

1 The line $y = kx$, between $0 \leqslant x \leqslant 3$, is rotated $360°$ around the x-axis to form a uniform conical shell. Show that the centre of mass is at $(2,0)$.

2 A conical shell is formed by rotating the line $y = 12 - 2x$, for $0 \leqslant x \leqslant 6$ through $360°$ around the x-axis.

(a) Find the coordinates of the centre of mass of the shell.

(b) The shell is placed on an inclined plane with its circular base in contact with the plane. Find the angle between the plane and the horizontal when the shell is on the point of toppling. Assume that the shell does not slide.

3 A hollow frustum is formed by rotating the line $y = 3x + 2$, for $1 \leqslant x \leqslant 7$ through 360° around the x-axis.

 (a) Find the coordinates of the centre of mass of this shell.

 (b) This hollow frustum is to hang so that its axis of symmetry is horizontal. Calculate the shortest distance between the rim of the top of the frustum and the point of suspension.

4 A hollow frustum is formed by rotating the line joining the points with coordinates $(1,1)$ and $(10, 10)$ through 360° about the x-axis.

 (a) Find the coordinates of the centre of mass of this shell.

 (b) The frustum is placed on an inclined plane with its larger circle in contact with the plane. Calculate the angle between the plane and the horizontal when the frustum is on the point of toppling. Assume that the frustum does not slide.

5 A conical shell is formed by rotating the line that joins the points with coordinates $(-3, 0)$ and $(21, 12)$ through 360° about the x-axis. Use integration to find the coordinates of the centre of mass of this shell.

6 A cardboard lampshade is made in the shape of a frustum, as shown below. Find the distance of the centre of mass of the frustum from the base.

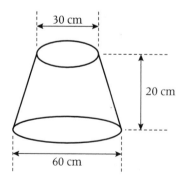

Key point summary

1 The lamina equations are used to find the centre of   *p89*
mass of a system of particles. They can also be used to
find the centre of mass of a composite lamina, that is, a
lamina which can be divided into separate shapes, the
centres of mass of which must be known.

2 When a rigid body is freely suspended from a fixed   *p92*
point the centre of mass of the body must be vertically
below the point of suspension.

3 The centre of mass of any solid that is formed by   *p98*
rotating a region through 360° around the *x*-axis can
be found by using the volume of revolution formulae.

4 When a body is placed on a slope inclined at an angle   *p99*
α to the horizontal, the greatest value for angle α for
which equilibrium is possible will be when the centre of
mass is vertically above the end point of contact.

Formulae

For a lamina

$$\bar{x} = \frac{\int_a^b xy\,dx}{\int_a^b y\,dx} \quad \text{or} \quad \bar{x} = \frac{1}{\text{Area}} \times \int_a^b xy\,dx$$

$$\bar{y} = \frac{\int_a^b \frac{1}{2}y^2\,dx}{\int_a^b y\,dx} \quad \text{or} \quad \bar{y} = \frac{1}{\text{Area}} \times \int_a^b \frac{1}{2}y^2\,dx$$

For a volume of revolution

$$\bar{x} = \frac{\int_a^b xy^2\,dx}{\int_a^b y^2\,dx}$$

For a shell formed by rotating a line around the *x*-axis

$$\bar{x} = \frac{\int_a^b xy\,dx}{\int_a^b y\,dx}$$

Test yourself	What to review

1 A uniform lamina consists of the region bounded by the lines $x = 0$, $x = 4$, $y = 0$ and the curve $y = (x - 2)^2 + 1$.

Section 4.1

   (a) Find the coordinates of the centre of mass of the lamina.

   (b) The lamina is suspended from the point that has coordinates $(0, 0)$. Find the angle between the side formed by the line $y = 0$ and the vertical when the lamina is in equilibrium.

---

2 The region bounded by the lines $x = 4$, $y = 0$ and the curve $y = \dfrac{x^2}{6}$, is rotated through 360° around the x-axis.

Section 4.2

   (a) Find the distance of the centre of mass from the y-axis.

   (b) The solid is placed on an inclined plane with the flat surface of the solid in contact with the plane. Find the angle between the plane and the horizontal when the solid is on the point of toppling. Assume that the solid does not slide down the plane.

---

3 Use integration to find the position of the centre of mass of a conical shell that has height 8 cm and base radius 3 cm.

Section 4.3

Test yourself ANSWERS

3 $\dfrac{16}{3}$ cm from the top.

2 (a) $\dfrac{10}{3}$,   **(b)** 76°.

1 (a) $(2, 1.47)$,   **(b)** 36.3°.

Application of differential equations in mechanics

Learning objectives

After studying this chapter you should be able to:

- use $\dfrac{dv}{dt}$ to form and solve differential equations to obtain relationships between velocity and time

- use $v\dfrac{dv}{dx}$ to form and solve differential equations to obtain relationships between velocity and displacement.

5.1 Introduction

In your earlier work you will have encountered situations where the acceleration of a body is given as a function of t.

> In these cases the function can be integrated directly to find the velocity and again to find the displacement.

For example, if you write $\dfrac{dv}{dt} = f(t)$, then v can be found using integration as $v = \displaystyle\int f(t)dt$.

However there are other cases that are not so straightforward, where the acceleration might depend on the velocity of the body. For example the acceleration of a skydiver varies with his or her velocity. These types of problems give rise to differential equations of the form $\dfrac{dv}{dt} = f(v)$. Differential equations of this type can often be solved using the technique of separation of variables. In this case you would obtain

$$\frac{1}{f(v)} \times \frac{dv}{dt} = 1$$

$$\int \frac{1}{f(v)} dv = \int 1 dt$$

$$= t + c$$

Problems of this type are very common and some are considered in the following examples.

Worked example 5.1

A boat of mass 500 kg is travelling at 8 m s^{-1}, when its outboard motor falls off. The boat travels in a straight line until it stops. Assume that it experiences a resistive force of magnitude 25v N when travelling at v m s^{-1}.

(a) Find an expression for the velocity of the boat at time t seconds after the motor has fallen off, in terms of t, the time since the motor fell off.

(b) How far does the boat travel in the first 5 seconds after the motor falls off?

Solution

(a) There will be a single horizontal force acting on the boat, which will be the resistance force, as shown in the diagram. As this opposes the motion, the resultant force can be written as $-25v$. Then applying Newton's second law gives

25v N

$$500\frac{dv}{dt} = -25v$$

or

$$\frac{1}{v} \times \frac{dv}{dt} = -\frac{1}{20}$$

An integral can now be formed and evaluated

$$\int \frac{1}{v}dv = \int -\frac{1}{20}dt$$

$$\ln|v| = -\frac{t}{20} + c$$

Since v will always be positive in this problem we can discard the modulus signs and solve the equation for v, to give

$$\ln v = -\frac{t}{20} + c$$

$$v = e^{-\frac{t}{20} + c}$$

$$= Ae^{-\frac{t}{20}}$$

Note how A has been used to replace e^c and simplify the equation. Initially the boat was moving at 8 m s^{-1}, so substituting $v = 8$ and $t = 0$, will allow us to find A.

$$8 = Ae^0$$

$$A = 8$$

$$v = 8e^{-\frac{t}{20}}$$

(b) The distance travelled can be found by integrating the expression for the velocity, with limits of integration of 0 and 5.

$$\text{Distance} = \int_0^5 8e^{-\frac{t}{20}}\,dt$$

$$= \left[-160e^{-\frac{t}{20}}\right]_0^5$$

$$= (-160e^{-\frac{5}{20}}) - (-160e^0)$$

$$= 35.4\,\text{m (to 3 sf)}$$

The integration involved in this problem does not cause too much difficulty as the function of v is simple to integrate. In reality situations are more complex because more than one force will often be acting. A parachutist is considered in the next example, illustrating a situation in which both gravity and a resistance force are significant.

Worked example 5.2

A parachutist of mass 60 kg experiences a resistance force of magnitude $300v$ N, when his speed is $v\,\text{m s}^{-1}$. He is travelling vertically downwards at $20\,\text{m s}^{-1}$, when his parachute opens.

(a) Determine the terminal velocity of the parachutist.

(b) Find an expression for the velocity of the parachutist t seconds after his parachute has opened.

(c) Find the time that it takes for the parachutist's velocity to reduce to $5\,\text{m s}^{-1}$.

Assume $g = 10\,\text{m s}^{-2}$.

Solution

(a) The first step is to find the resultant force acting on the parachutist. The diagram shows the two forces acting, with the parachutist modelled as a particle. Taking the downward direction as positive, gives the resultant force as $600 - 300v$.

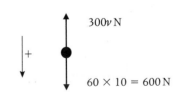

When at his terminal velocity the resultant force on the parachutist will be zero, giving

$$600 - 300v = 0$$

$$v = 2\,\text{m s}^{-1}$$

(b) Applying Newton's second law to the parachutist above gives

$$60\frac{dv}{dt} = 600 - 300v$$

$$\frac{dv}{dt} = -5(v - 2)$$

or

$$\frac{1}{v-2} \times \frac{dv}{dt} = -5$$

Integrating then gives

$$\int \frac{1}{v-2} dv = \int -5dt$$

$$\ln|v - 2| = -5t + c$$

As the velocity will decrease from 20 m s^{-1} towards the terminal velocity of 2 m s^{-1}, $v - 2$ will always be positive and so you can disregard the modulus signs. Then solving for v gives

$$\ln(v - 2) = -5t + c$$

$$v - 2 = e^{-5t + c}$$

$$v = 2 + e^{-5t + c}$$

$$= 2 + Ae^{-5t}$$

Note that e^c has again been replaced by A. As the initial velocity of the parachutist was 20 m s^{-1}, you can substitute $v = 20$ and $t = 0$, to find A.

$$20 = 2 + Ae^0$$

$$A = 18$$

$$v = 2 + 18e^{-5t}$$

(c) You must solve the equation

$$5 = 2 + 18e^{-5t}$$

$$3 = 18e^{-5t}$$

$$\tfrac{1}{6} = e^{-5t}$$

$$-5t = \ln\left(\frac{1}{6}\right)$$

$$t = \frac{1}{5} \ln 6 = 0.36 \text{ seconds (to 2 sf)}$$

Worked example 5.3

As a sphere, of mass 0.8 kg, falls vertically from rest through a fluid it experiences a resistance force of magnitude $32v^2$ N when travelling at v m s^{-1}.

(a) Find the terminal velocity of the sphere.

(b) Find the time it takes for the velocity of the sphere to reach
$0.4\,\text{m s}^{-1}$.

Assume that $g = 10\,\text{m s}^{-2}$.

Solution

(a) First consider the resultant force acting on the sphere. The
diagram shows the two forces present. Taking the
downward direction as positive gives the resultant force as
$8 - 32v^2$.

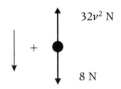

At its terminal velocity the resultant force on the sphere will
be zero, which gives

$$8 - 32v^2 = 0$$
$$v^2 = \frac{8}{32}$$
$$v = \sqrt{\frac{1}{4}} = \frac{1}{2}\text{m s}^{-1}$$

(b) First apply Newton's second law to obtain a differential
equation.

$$8 - 32v^2 = 0.8\frac{dv}{dt}$$

$$10 - 40v^2 = \frac{dv}{dt}$$

The variables can then be separated and integrated

$$10 = \frac{1}{1 - 4v^2}\frac{dv}{dt}$$

$$\int 10dt = \int \frac{1}{1 - 4v^2}dv$$

To integrate the right-hand side, first note that

$$\frac{1}{1 - 4v^2} = \frac{1}{(1 + 2v)(1 - 2v)}$$

Partial fractions can then be used to enable the integral to
be evaluated.

$$\frac{1}{(1 + 2v)(1 - 2v)} = \frac{A}{1 + 2v} + \frac{B}{1 - 2v}$$

The values of A and B are both $\dfrac{1}{2}$, so the integral becomes

$$\int 10dt = \int \frac{1}{2(1 + 2v)} + \frac{1}{2(1 - 2v)}dv$$

Now the integration can be carried out to give

$$10t + c = \frac{1}{4}\ln|1 + 2v| - \frac{1}{4}\ln|1 - 2v|$$

As the terminal velocity is $\frac{1}{2}$ m s^{-1}, both $1 + 2v$ and $1 - 2v$ will always be positive and so the modulus signs can be removed. Using the initial conditions $v = 0$ when $t = 0$, allows the constant of integration to be found. Substituting the values above gives

$$c = \frac{1}{4}\ln 1 - \frac{1}{4}\ln 1$$

$$c = 0$$

With this value for c you have

$$10t = \frac{1}{4}\ln\left(1 + 2v\right) - \frac{1}{4}\ln\left(1 - 2v\right)$$

Now find the time when $v = 0.4$

$$10t = \frac{1}{4}\ln(1 + 2 \times 0.4) - \frac{1}{4}\ln(1 - 2 \times 0.4)$$

$$10t = \frac{1}{4}\ln\left(\frac{1.8}{0.2}\right)$$

$$t = \frac{1}{40}\ln 9 = 0.055 \text{ seconds (to 2 sf)}$$

EXERCISE 5A

1   A particle, of mass 2 kg, is set into motion on a smooth horizontal surface. Its initial velocity is 20 m s^{-1}. When moving at v m s^{-1}, it experiences a resistance force of magnitude $5v$ N.

   (a) Find an expression for the velocity of the particle after t seconds.

   (b) Find an expression for the distance travelled by the particle after t seconds.

   (c) How far does the particle travel?

2   A particle, of mass 4 kg, moves horizontally along a straight line and is subject to a resistance force of magnitude $2v^2$ N, when moving at v m s^{-1}. Find an expression for the velocity of the particle at time t seconds, if the initial velocity of the particle is

   (a) 5 m s^{-1},   **(b)** 20 m s^{-1}.

3   A torpedo is fired horizontally from a stationary submarine at a speed of 80 m s^{-1}. The torpedo has a mass of 100 kg and is subject to a resistance force of magnitude $50v$ N, when travelling at a speed of v m s^{-1}.

   (a) Find an expression for the speed of the torpedo at time t seconds.

(b) Find an expression for the distance travelled by the torpedo in t seconds.

(c) Find the distance travelled by the torpedo when its speed has dropped to $20 \, \text{m s}^{-1}$.

4 A child is travelling at $6 \, \text{m s}^{-1}$, when she reaches the bottom of a slide. She then moves onto a rough horizontal surface. The coefficient of friction between the horizontal surface and the child is 0.2.

(a) Find an expression for the speed of the child when she has been moving for t seconds on the horizontal surface, if there is no air resistance present.

The child, who has mass m kg, also experiences an air resistance force of magnitude $2mv \, \text{N}$ when travelling at $v \, \text{m s}^{-1}$.

(b) Assume that the surface is smooth and that only the air resistance acts to slow down the child. Find expressions for the speed at time t seconds.

(c) If both air resistance and friction act, find an expression for the speed of the child at time t seconds.

(d) For each case considered above find the speed of the child after 0.5 seconds. Comment on your results.

5 A sphere, of mass m kg, falls vertically from rest in a fluid. It experiences a resistive force of magnitude $4mv \, \text{N}$, when travelling at $v \, \text{m s}^{-1}$.

(a) Find an expression for the velocity of the sphere after it has been falling for t seconds. Give your answer in terms of g.

(b) Find an expression for the distance fallen after t seconds.

(c) Find when the sphere reaches 90% of its terminal speed and the distance travelled in this time.

6 A boat of mass 200 kg experiences a constant forward force of 120 N and a resistive force that has magnitude $25v \, \text{N}$, when the boat is travelling at $v \, \text{m s}^{-1}$. Find expressions for the velocity and displacement of the boat at time t seconds, if the boat starts at rest at the origin.

7 A particle, of mass m kg, is allowed to fall from rest. It experiences a resistance force of magnitude $mkv \, \text{N}$ when falling at $v \, \text{m s}^{-1}$.

Find in terms of g and k expressions for

(a) the velocity of the particle at time t seconds

(b) the distance fallen by the particle at time t seconds.

8 A particle, of mass 5 kg, and initially at rest, is pulled horizontally on a smooth horizontal surface. A constant horizontal force of 20 N acts on the particle. It also experiences a resistance force of magnitude $5v^2$ N, when travelling at v m s^{-1}.

   (a) Find the maximum speed that the particle will reach.

   (b) Find the time it takes for the particle to reach half of its maximum speed.

9 A particle experiences a retardation of $0.005v^4$ m s^{-2}, when it travels at a speed of v m s^{-1}. It has an initial speed of 10 m s^{-1}.

   (a) Find the time when the speed has dropped to 5 m s^{-1}.

   (b) Find the speed after 2 seconds.

10 A particle of mass 4 kg is released from rest and falls under gravity against a resistance to motion of $2v$ N where v is velocity in m s^{-1}.

   Determine its terminal velocity. How long does it take to reach a velocity of 15 m s^{-1}?

11 Two small stones, each of mass m, are allowed to fall through a fluid. One is released from rest 2 seconds after the other. Assume that they are each subjected to a resistance force of magnitude mkv, where k is a constant and v the speed of the stone.

   (a) State **two** factors on which the value of k could depend.

   (b) Show that the acceleration of the first stone will be $g - kv$, when its speed is v.

   Hence show that the speed of this stone at time t is given by
   $$v = \frac{g}{k}(1 - e^{-kt})$$
   and find an expression for the distance, x, fallen by the first stone in time t.

   (c) Write down an expression for the distance fallen by a second stone, when the first stone has been falling for t seconds, and then find the distance between the two stones at this time.

   (d) What will happen to the distance between the stones after a long time?   [A]

12 A skydiver of mass m falls vertically and, in addition to the constant gravitational force, she experiences a resistance of magnitude mkv, where k is a constant and v is her speed. Show that at time t
   $$\frac{dv}{dt} = g - kv.$$

Prove that, after falling for a time T from the point where her speed is W, her speed, v, is given by

$$kv = g(1 - e^{-kT}) + kWe^{-kT}$$

On a particular occasion the skydiver falls from rest. After falling for 5 seconds she opens her parachute, which has the effect of increasing the value of k from $0.2 \, \text{s}^{-1}$ to $2.0 \, \text{s}^{-1}$.

Calculate the speed of the skydiver

(a) immediately before the parachute opens

(b) when she has been falling for 6 seconds. [A]

13 The motion of a cyclist on a horizontal surface is to be modelled based on the following assumptions:

● The cycle and cyclist are to be modelled as a single particle of mass m kg.
● A constant forward force of magnitude F N acts on the particle.
● A resistance force of magnitude kv N acts on the particle when it is travelling at a speed of $v \, \text{m s}^{-1}$.

(a) Show that at time t seconds the speed v of the cyclist is given by

$$v = \frac{F - Ae^{-\frac{kt}{m}}}{k}$$

where A is a constant.

(b) The cyclist starts at rest and moves at a speed of $6 \, \text{m s}^{-1}$ after 5 seconds. The maximum speed that the cyclist can attain is $8 \, \text{m s}^{-1}$. Show that

$$v = 8\left(1 - e^{-\frac{t \ln 4}{5}}\right)$$
[A]

5.2 Alternative form for the acceleration of a body

There is an alternative form for the acceleration of a body that can be used when looking for a relationship between velocity and displacement, rather than between velocity and time.

Using the chain rule

$$\frac{dv}{dt} = \frac{dx}{dt} \times \frac{dv}{dx}$$

$$= v\frac{dv}{dx}$$

You can now see some examples where this alternative form for the acceleration can be used.

Worked example 5.4

A particle, of mass 4 kg, slides on a smooth surface subject to a resistance force of magnitude $10v$ N, when travelling at v m s^{-1}. The particle has an initial speed of 20 m s^{-1}.

$10v$ N

(a) Find an expression for the velocity of the particle when it has travelled a distance x m.

(b) How far does the particle travel before it stops?

Solution

(a) The resultant force on the particle is $-10v$, so applying Newton's second law, with $v\dfrac{dv}{dx}$ for the acceleration, gives

$$4v\frac{dv}{dx} = -10v$$

$$\frac{dv}{dx} = -2.5$$

This can be integrated directly to give

$$v = -2.5x + c$$

The initial condition $v = 20$, when $x = 0$ allows the value of c to be found.

$$20 = -2.5 \times 0 + c$$

$$c = 20$$

So the velocity is given by $v = 20 - 2.5x$.

(b) The particle stops when $v = 0$, so

$$0 = 20 - 2.5x$$

$$x = \frac{20}{2.5}$$

$$= 8 \text{ m}$$

Worked example 5.5

A model for the resistance force on a freewheeling car is based on the assumption that this force is proportional to the square of the speed of the car. An experiment is conducted in which a car is driven to a speed of 30 m s^{-1}, and then allowed to freewheel until it stops. As the car travels a distance of 50 m, its speed is reduced to 15 m s^{-1}.

(a) Find an expression for the speed, $v\,\text{m s}^{-1}$, of the car when it has travelled $x\,\text{m}$.

(b) Calculate the speed of the car when it has travelled 25 m.

Solution

(a) The resultant force on the car will be $-mkv^2$ N, where k is a positive constant and m kg the mass of the car. Applying Newton's second law with the acceleration in the form $v\dfrac{dv}{dx}$ gives

$$-mkv^2 = mv\frac{dv}{dx}$$

$$-kv = \frac{dv}{dx}$$

$$\int \frac{1}{v}dv = \int -k\,dx$$

$$\ln|v| = -kx + c$$

$$v = Ae^{-kx}$$

Using $\quad x = 50$ at $v = 15$

gives $\quad 15 = 30e^{-50k}$

$$k = \frac{1}{50}\ln 2$$

Hence $\quad v = 30e^{-\frac{x}{50}\ln 2}$

(b) Substitute $x = 25$ into the expression for v to obtain the speed.

$$v = 30e^{-\frac{25}{50}\ln 2}$$

$$= 21.2\,\text{m s}^{-1}$$

Worked example 5.6

A toy projects a clown of mass 250 grams vertically upwards at an initial speed of $3\,\text{m s}^{-1}$. The clown is subject to gravity and a resistance force of magnitude $0.5v$ N when moving at $v\,\text{m s}^{-1}$. Find the displacement of the clown in terms of v and the maximum height of the clown.

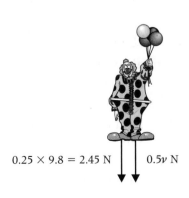

$0.25 \times 9.8 = 2.45$ N $\qquad 0.5v$ N

Solution

The first stage is to find an expression that links velocity and displacement. As the resultant force on the clown is $-(0.5v + 0.25 \times 9.8)$ we can apply Newton's second law to give

$$0.25v\frac{dv}{dx} = -(0.5v + 2.45)$$

$$v\frac{dv}{dx} = -2(v + 4.9)$$

$$\frac{v}{v + 4.9}\frac{dv}{dx} = -2$$

$$\int\frac{v}{v + 4.9}\,dv = \int -2dx$$

The left-hand integral can be simplified by noting that

$$\frac{v}{v + 4.9} = 1 - \frac{4.9}{v + 4.9}$$

This allows the integration to be carried out.

$$\int 1 - \frac{4.9}{v + 4.9}\,dv = \int -2dx$$

$$v - 4.9\ln(v + 4.9) = -2x + c$$

Using the initial conditions $v = 3$ when $x = 0$ allows the value of c to be found.

$$3 - 4.9\ln 7.9 = c$$

Substituting this value for c gives

$$v - 4.9\ln(v + 4.9) = -2x + 3 - 4.9\ln 7.9$$

$$x = \frac{1}{2}\left(3 - v + 4.9\ln\left(\frac{v + 4.9}{7.9}\right)\right)$$

The maximum height will be achieved when $v = 0$. This gives

$$x = \frac{1}{2}\left(3 - 0 + 4.9\ln\left(\frac{0 + 4.9}{7.9}\right)\right)$$

$$= 0.330 \text{ m or } 33.0 \text{ cm.}$$

EXERCISE 5B

1 A particle, of mass 20 kg, moves horizontally on a smooth surface subject to a resistance force of magnitude $4v$ N. It has an initial speed of 20 m s^{-1}.

   (a) Find the speed of the particle when it has travelled x m.

   (b) Find the distance that the particle has travelled when it comes to rest.

2 A boat, of mass 400 kg, is initially travelling at 6 m s^{-1}, when its engine stops. The boat then slows down moving in a straight line. If the magnitude of the resistance force is $2v^2 \text{ N}$, when the speed of the boat is $v \text{ m s}^{-1}$, find how far the boat travels before its speed drops to 1 m s^{-1}.

3 A bullet, of mass 50 grams, is fired horizontally at an initial speed of 120 m s^{-1}. It hits a target 50 m from the point where it was fired. The bullet is subject to a resistance force of magnitude $0.001v^2 \text{ N}$. Assume that any vertical motion of the bullet can be neglected. Find the speed of the bullet when it hits the target.

4 A sphere, of mass 100 grams, falling vertically from rest through a fluid experiences a resistive force of magnitude $0.1v^2 \text{ N}$, where $v \text{ m s}^{-1}$ is the speed of the sphere. Find the speed of the sphere when it has fallen a distance of 1 m.

5 A particle, of mass 4 kg, slides on a rough horizontal surface. It is subject to a resistance force of magnitude $8v^2 \text{ N}$, when travelling at $v \text{ m s}^{-1}$. The coefficient of friction between the particle and the plane is 0.5.

   (a) Show that $\dfrac{v}{2.45 + v^2}\dfrac{dv}{dx} = -2$.

   (b) Hence show that $\ln(2.45 + v^2) = -4x + c$.

   (c) Find c if the initial speed of the particle is 5 m s^{-1}.

   (d) How far does the particle travel before it comes to rest?

6 A small sphere, of mass 0.2 kg, falls vertically from rest under the influence of gravity and subject to a resistance force of magnitude $2v \text{ N}$, where the speed of the particle is $v \text{ m s}^{-1}$.

   (a) Show that $\dfrac{v}{v - 0.98}\dfrac{dv}{dx} = -10$.

   (b) Verify that $\dfrac{v}{v - 0.98} = 1 + \dfrac{0.98}{v - 0.98}$.

   (c) Hence show that $v + 0.98 \ln|v - 0.98| = -10x + c$.

   (d) Find c.

   (e) Find the distance that the sphere has fallen when its speed is 0.5 m s^{-1}.

7 A ball, of mass m kg, is thrown vertically upwards with an initial velocity $U \text{ m s}^{-1}$. It experiences a resistance force of magnitude $\dfrac{mv^2}{k} \text{ N}$, where k is a constant, when moving at $v \text{ m s}^{-1}$.

   (a) Show that $\dfrac{v}{v^2 + gk}\dfrac{dv}{dx} = -\dfrac{1}{k}$ where x is the displacement of the sphere.

   (b) Verify that $\ln(v^2 + gk) = 2\left(c - \dfrac{x}{k}\right)$.

   (c) Find the maximum height of the ball.

8 A particle of mass m moves along a straight line under the action of a resisting force of magnitude $\dfrac{mv^2}{b}$, where v is the speed of the particle and b is a positive constant. The particle passes through a point O with speed u. Show that, when it is at a distance x from O, its speed is $ue^{-x/b}$. [A]

9 A particle of mass 1 kg is released from rest and falls under gravity against resistance of $\dfrac{v^2}{2}$ N where v is its velocity in m s^{-1}. Determine its terminal velocity. How far does the body fall as its velocity increases from 2 m s^{-1} to 4 m s^{-1}?

10 A submarine fires a torpedo, of mass m, horizontally into the water at a speed of 30 m s^{-1}. It continues to move horizontally subject to a resistance force of magnitude mkv^3, where k is a constant and v is the speed of the torpedo at time t. The torpedo hits a target, which is 100 m away from the submarine, at a speed of 10 m s^{-1}.

(a) Find an expression for $\dfrac{dv}{dt}$ and show that
$$\frac{1}{v^2} = 2kt + \frac{1}{900}.$$

(b) Also show that
$$\frac{1}{v} = kx + \frac{1}{30}$$
where x is the distance of the torpedo from the submarine at time t.

(c) Find the time the torpedo takes to reach the target. [A]

11 A cyclist is travelling at a speed of 8 m s^{-1} when she stops pedalling. Without braking, she freewheels in a straight line until the cycle comes to rest. All the motion takes place on a horizontal road.

(a) State two of the factors that are most significant in determining the time that it takes for the cyclist to stop.

Assume that, when the cyclist stops pedalling, the only force that affects the motion of the cycle is air resistance which is proportional to the speed of the cyclist. The mass of the cycle and the cyclist is 60 kg.

(b) Show that the speed of the cyclist, v m s^{-1}, is given by $v = 8 - \dfrac{kx}{60}$, where x m is the distance that the cyclist has travelled since she stopped pedalling and k is a constant. Find the value of k, if she travels 20 m before stopping.

(c) Find the time that it takes for the speed of the cyclist to drop from 8 m s^{-1} to 2 m s^{-1}. [A]

12 The maximum power output of an engine on a small boat is 4800 W and the boat has a top speed of 8 m s^{-1}. The mass of the boat and its occupants is 300 kg.

Two possible models for the resistance force acting on the boat are (either) that it is proportional to:

    A   the speed of the boat   or

    B   the square of the speed of the boat.

The boat is travelling at its top speed when the engine is switched off and the boat allowed to drift until it comes to rest.

(a) Use model A to show that $v = 8e^{-0.25t}$, where v is the speed at time t, and hence find an expression for the distance travelled in time t. Find the distance that the boat travels before it stops.

(b) Use model B for the resistance to show that $v = 8e^{-\frac{x}{32}}$ where x is the distance travelled at time t, and find the distance that this model predicts the boat will travel before it stops.

(c) Explain which of these models is more realistic, giving reasons for your choice.   [A]

13 A particle, of mass 1 kg, is projected on a smooth horizontal surface with an initial speed of 20 m s^{-1}. It experiences a resistance force proportional to the square of its speed. At time t seconds it has travelled x metres and is moving at speed v m s^{-1}.

(a) Show that
$$v = Ae^{-kx}$$
and
$$v = \frac{1}{kt - c} \text{ where } A, k \text{ and } c \text{ are constants.}$$

(b) Find the values of A and c.

(c) If the speed of the particle drops to 5 m s^{-1} after 2 seconds, find the distance that the particle has travelled.

14 Children emerge from a long curved slide, AB, and then travel on a horizontal surface, BC, until they stop. The diagram shows the slide.

On the horizontal section, BC, a child travelling with a speed of v m s^{-1} experiences an air resistance force of magnitude $20v$ N. In this question consider a child of mass 40 kg, who is travelling at 5 m s^{-1} at the start of the horizontal section.

A simple model assumes that the surface is smooth and that the children stop due to the effects of air resistance only.

(a) Show that the child travels 10 m before stopping.

A revised model assumes that the child experiences a friction force as well as the air resistance. Assume that the friction force has magnitude 80 N.

(b) Show that for the revised model,

$$v\frac{dv}{dx} = -\frac{1}{2}(v + 4),$$

where v m s^{-1} is the velocity of the child when she has travelled x metres.

(c) Given that $\dfrac{v}{v + 4} = 1 - \dfrac{4}{v + 4}$, show that the revised model predicts the child will travel approximately 3.5 m before stopping.

(d) In the light of your answers to parts **(a)** and **(c)**, comment on the value of the model that ignores friction. [A]

15 A cannon fires a cannon-ball, of mass 10 kg, at a stationary trolley, of mass 100 kg. The trolley is 5 m from the cannon. The cannon-ball leaves the cannon travelling horizontally at 80 m s^{-1} and becomes embedded in the trolley on impact.

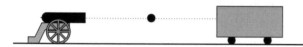

(a) Explain why it would be reasonable to assume that the cannon-ball is travelling horizontally when it hits the trolley. Justify your answer by using suitable calculations.

(b) A simple model assumes that the cannon-ball hits the trolley with the same velocity that it left the cannon. Find the speeds at which the trolley and cannon-ball move after impact.

A revised model for the motion of the cannon-ball takes account of air resistance and assumes that this is a force of magnitude $\dfrac{v^2}{40}$ N, when the cannon-ball is travelling at a speed of v m s^{-1}.

(c) Use this model for air resistance to find the speed of the cannon-ball when it hits the trolley. Use this speed to revise your answer to part **(b)**.

(d) Does including air resistance make a significant difference to the predicted speed of the trolley? Give a reason to justify your answer. [A]

Key point summary

1 $\dfrac{dv}{dt}$ can be used to form and solve differential
   equations to obtain relationships between velocity
   and time.   *p111*

2 $v\dfrac{dv}{dx}$ can be used to form and solve differential
   equations to obtain relationships between velocity
   and displacement.   *p119*

Test yourself	What to review

1 A particle, of mass 2 kg, slides horizontally on a smooth
   surface subject to a resistance force of magnitude $2v$ N,
   when travelling at v m s^{-1}. The initial speed of the particle
   is 10 m s^{-1}.   *Section 5.1*

   (a) Find the speed of the particle after 2 seconds.

   (b) Find the distance travelled by the particle in the first
   2 seconds

2 A ball, of mass 0.1 kg, is projected vertically upwards with an   *Section 5.2*
   initial speed of 10 m s^{-1}. It is acted on by gravity and a
   resistance force. The magnitude of the resistance force is $2v$ N,
   when travelling at v m s^{-1}. Find the time that it takes the ball
   to reach its maximum height.

3 A cyclist starts to freewheel, while travelling at 8 m s^{-1}. The   *Sections 5.2*
   cyclist experiences a resistance force, of magnitude $3v^2$ N
   when travelling at a speed of v m s^{-1}. The cyclist and her cycle
   have a total mass of 75 kg. How far has the cyclist travelled
   by the time that her speed drops to 4 m s^{-1}?

Test yourself ANSWERS

3 17.3 m

2 0.153 s.

1 **(a)** 1.35 m s^{-1} **(c)** 8.65 m.

CHAPTER 6

Simple harmonic motion

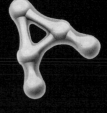

Learning objectives

After studying this chapter you should be able to:

- show that for simple harmonic motion to take place $\dfrac{d^2x}{dt^2} = -\omega^2 x$
- apply the equation $v^2 = \omega^2(a^2 - x^2)$
- find the period of the motion using period $= \dfrac{2\pi}{\omega}$
- use the term amplitude
- express the displacement of a body describing SHM in one of the following forms:
  $x = A \sin \omega t$
  $x = A \cos \omega t$
  $x = A \cos \omega t + B \sin \omega t.$

6.1 Introduction

Simple harmonic motion can be found in many simple situations. Many things that move up and down or from side to side will have simple harmonic motion or motion that can be approximated by simple harmonic motion. One of the examples that you will meet in this chapter is the motion of a mass that is suspended from a spring. Other examples could include the motion of the blade in a jigsaw, the needle in a sewing machine or the pendulum in a clock.

Definition

The motion of a particle is said to be simple harmonic when its acceleration is proportional to its displacement from a fixed point, O, such that the acceleration is always directed towards O.

Let the displacement of a particle from O be x. If the acceleration $\left(\dfrac{d^2x}{dt^2}\right)$ of the particle is proportional to x, then

$$\frac{d^2x}{dt^2} = kx$$

But, if the acceleration is directed towards O, then $k < 0$, so that we can write

$$\frac{d^2x}{dt^2} = -\omega^2 x$$

The minus sign in this equation is vital to the definition of simple harmonic motion (SHM). The constant of proportionality is put in the form of ω^2 to make the formulae, which result from this equation more manageable.

The above equation can be taken as the definition of SHM. In problems that you will meet later in this chapter, it will be required to prove that a particle executes SHM, this will be accomplished by showing that its acceleration satisfies the equation above.

For simple harmonic motion to take place

$$\frac{d^2x}{dt^2} = -\omega^2 x$$

The nature of the motion

The acceleration of a particle can be written as $\dfrac{d^2x}{dt^2}$ or $v\dfrac{dv}{dx}$ $\left(\text{where } v = \dfrac{dx}{dt}\right)$. If a particle executes SHM then

$$v\frac{dv}{dx} = -\omega^2 x$$

The variables can be separated in this equation to give

$$\int v\,dv = -\omega^2 \int x\,dx$$
$$\tfrac{1}{2}v^2 = -\tfrac{1}{2}\omega^2 x^2 + c \text{ where } c \text{ is a constant and } C = 2c,$$
i.e. $\quad v^2 = C - \omega^2 x^2$

There are three important conclusions, which can be drawn from this equation:

(i)   The velocity v decreases as x increases. In fact there will be a value of x for which $v = 0$, when the particle is at its maximum displacement from O. If $v = 0$, when $x = a$, we can write C in terms of a

$$0^2 = C - \omega^2 a^2 \quad \Rightarrow \quad C = \omega^2 a^2$$
$$v^2 = \omega^2 a^2 - \omega^2 x^2$$

$$v^2 = \omega^2(a^2 - x^2)$$

(ii) The equation is an even function of x. Hence, if $v = 0$ when $x = a$, then $v = 0$ also when $x = -a$.

> The constant a gives the greatest distance of the particle from O, and is called the **amplitude** of the motion.

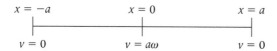

$$x = -a \qquad x = 0 \qquad x = a$$
$$v = 0 \qquad v = a\omega \qquad v = 0$$

(iii) The speed increases as $|x|$ decreases. The maximum speed occurs at O, and is given by

$$v_{\max} = a\omega \qquad\qquad (3)$$

When a particle executes SHM it will move backwards and forwards between two fixed points. The centre of the motion ($x = 0$) is called the equilibrium position. This is because the acceleration is zero here.

Also note that the acceleration is a maximum at the end points. To determine the time taken for the particle to complete an oscillation we can substitute $v = \dfrac{dx}{dt}$ in the equation $v^2 = \omega^2(a^2 - x^2)$ to give

$$\left(\frac{dx}{dt}\right)^2 = \omega^2(a^2 - x^2)$$

$$\therefore \frac{dx}{dt} = \pm\omega^2\sqrt{a^2 - x^2}$$

Taking the positive root gives

$$\frac{dx}{dt} = \omega\sqrt{a^2 - x^2}$$

The variables can then be separated and the expression integrated to give

$$\int \frac{1}{\sqrt{a^2 - x^2}}\, dx = \omega \int dt$$

$$\sin^{-1}\left(\frac{x}{a}\right) = \omega t + c$$

$$x = a \sin(\omega t + c)$$

Where c is an arbitrary constant, which will be determined by the initial conditions.

Two particular initial conditions are common:

(i) the particle starts (i.e. $t = 0$) at $x = 0$
$$0 = a \sin c \Rightarrow \sin c = 0 \qquad \therefore c = 0 \Rightarrow x = a \sin \omega t$$

(ii) The particle starts at $x = a$.

$$a = a \sin c \Rightarrow \sin c = 1 \qquad \therefore c = \frac{\pi}{2}$$

$$x = a \sin \left(\omega t + \frac{\pi}{2}\right)$$

but $\sin \left(\theta + \frac{\pi}{2}\right) \equiv \cos \theta \Rightarrow x = a \cos \omega t$

Sometimes, however, questions can be set where the starting position is unknown. An alternative to the equation $x = a \sin (\omega t + c)$ is available. The function $\sin (\omega t + c)$ can be expanded:

$$a \sin (\omega t + c) = a \sin \omega t \cos c + a \cos \omega t \sin c$$

but a and c are constants, so

$$a \sin (\omega t + c) = A \sin \omega t + B \cos \omega t$$

where A and B are arbitrary constants. So there may be times when it is better to use an equation of this form to describe SHM.

$$x = A \sin \omega t + B \cos \omega t$$

> The period of the motion is independent of the starting position and is determined by the period of the sine function. The function $\sin (\omega t + c)$ completes a full cycle when ωt increases by 2π. The time for one complete cycle is given by, $\omega t = 2\pi$
>
> $$\text{Period} = \frac{2\pi}{\omega}$$

The frequency (number of cycles per second), is given by

$$f = \frac{1}{\text{period}} = \frac{\omega}{2\pi}.$$

Worked example 6.1

A particle performs SHM at 10 cycles per second, with amplitude 20 cm. Find its maximum speed.

Solution

Recall that the maximum speed is given by $a\omega$, the first step is to find ω. As the particle completes 10 cycles per second it will have a period of 0.1 seconds. Then using Period $= \dfrac{2\pi}{\omega}$ gives

$$0.1 = \frac{\pi}{\omega}$$
$$\omega = 20\pi$$

Now we can find the maximum speed, noting that $a = 0.2$

$$v_{\text{max}} = a\omega$$
$$= 0.2 \times 20\pi$$
$$= 12.6 \text{ m s}^{-1}.$$

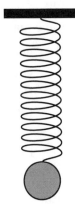

Worked example 6.2

A mass is suspended from a spring. The displacement of the mass from its equilibrium position is x m. The motion of the mass is governed by the equation $\dfrac{d^2x}{dt^2} = -25x$. The maximum speed of the particle is π m s^{-1}. Find the amplitude and period of the motion.

Solution

Using the definition of SHM, $\dfrac{d^2x}{dt^2} = -\omega^2 x$ gives

$$\omega^2 = 25$$
$$\omega = 5$$

Then using period $= \dfrac{2\pi}{\omega}$ gives

$$\text{Period} = \frac{2\pi}{\omega} = \frac{2\pi}{5}\,\text{s}$$

The fact that the maximum speed is given by $v_{\max} = a\omega$ can be used to find the amplitude of the motion.

$$\pi = a \times \frac{2\pi}{5}$$
$$a = 2.5 \text{ m}.$$

Worked example 6.3

A particle performs SHM about an origin O. The displacement of the particle from O is x m. When $x = 1$ m its speed is 2 m s^{-1}, and when $x = 2$ m its speed is 1 m s^{-1}. Find the period and amplitude of the motion.

Solution

Using $v^2 = \omega^2(a^2 - x^2)$ you can obtain a pair of simultaneous equations by substituting the velocity and displacement at each position.

$$x = 1 \text{ and } v = 2 \text{ gives} \qquad 4 = \omega^2(a^2 - 1)$$
$$x = 2 \text{ and } v = 1 \text{ gives} \qquad 1 = \omega^2(a^2 - 4)$$

Dividing these equations gives

$$\frac{4}{1} = \frac{\omega^2(a^2 - 1)}{\omega^2(a^2 - 4)}$$
$$4 = \frac{(a^2 - 1)}{(a^2 - 4)}$$
$$4a^2 - 16 = a^2 - 1$$
$$3a^2 = 15$$
$$a = \sqrt{5}$$

So the amplitude of the motion is $\sqrt{5} = 2.24$ m (to 3 sf).

Substitute $a = \sqrt{5}$ into the first of the two simultaneous equations to find ω.

$$4 = \omega^2(5 - 1)$$
$$\omega = 1$$

The period can now be calculated.

$$\text{Period} = \frac{2\pi}{\omega} \text{ or } 6.28 \text{ s (to 3 sf)}$$

Worked example 6.4

A spot of light moves with SHM. The amplitude of the motion is 5 m and its period is 8 s. The displacement of the spot from its central position, at time t, is x. Find the time taken by the particle to move from A, the point where $x = 3$, directly to the point B, where $x = -2$.

Solution

Assume that $x = 5$ when $t = 0$, so that initially $x = 5$ and the amplitude of the motion is 5 m. Then you can write

$$x = 5 \cos \omega t.$$

Then consider the period to find ω.

$$\text{Period} = \frac{2\pi}{\omega} = 8$$
$$\omega = \frac{\pi}{4}.$$

So the displacement at time t seconds is given by,

$$x = 5 \cos \frac{\pi}{4} t$$

The graph shows how the displacement varies with time.

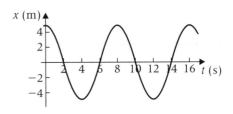

If t_1 is the time taken to travel to A, and t_2 is the time taken to travel to B, then the required time will be given by $t_2 - t_1$. To find t_1, substitute $x = 3$.

$$3 = 5 \cos \frac{\pi}{4} t_1$$

$$t_1 = 1.18 \text{ s}$$

To find t_2, substitute $x = -2$.

$$2 = 5 \cos \frac{\pi}{4} t_2$$

$$t_2 = 2.52 \text{ s}.$$

Finally

$$t_2 - t_1 = 1.34 \text{ s}.$$

Worked example 6.5

The displacement of a particle, P, from an origin O, is given by

$$x = 2 \cos 3t + 5 \sin 3t.$$

Show that the acceleration of P is proportional to its displacement from O.

Solution

First differentiate to find $\dfrac{d^2x}{dt^2}$ in terms of t.

$$x = 2 \cos 3t + 5 \sin 3t$$

$$\frac{dx}{dt} = -6 \sin 3t + 15 \cos 3t$$

$$\frac{d^2x}{dt^2} = -18 \cos 3t - 45 \sin 3t$$

$$= -9 \,(2 \cos 3t + 5 \sin 3t)$$

Now this can be compared with the expression for x, which gives

$$\frac{d^2x}{dt^2} = -9x, \text{ so that we have SHM.}$$

Worked example 6.6

The motion of a particle, P, is defined by $\dfrac{d^2x}{dt^2} = -16x$, where x is

the displacement of P from a fixed point O. When $t = \dfrac{\pi}{8}$, $x = 5$

and when $t = \dfrac{3\pi}{16}$, $x = \dfrac{3\sqrt{2}}{2}$.

Find: (a) the displacement of P at time t

(b) the displacement of P at time $t = 0$

(c) the speed of P when $t = 0$

(d) the amplitude of the motion.

Solution

As it is not known where the particle starts from, or what the amplitude is, use

$$x = A \cos \omega t + B \sin \omega t.$$

The constants A and B can be found from simultaneous equations given by the stated positions in the question.

(a) First find ω. If $\dfrac{d^2x}{dt^2} = -16x$, then $\omega = \sqrt{16} = 4$.

Substituting this value gives

$$x = A \cos 4t + B \sin 4t$$

Now substitute $x = 5$, when $t = \dfrac{\pi}{8}$

$$5 = A \cos\left(\frac{\pi}{2}\right) + B \sin\left(\frac{\pi}{2}\right)$$
$$5 = 0 + B$$
$$B = 5$$

When $t = \dfrac{3\pi}{16}$, $x = \dfrac{3\sqrt{2}}{2}$. Substituting these values gives

$$\frac{3\sqrt{2}}{2} = A \cos\left(\frac{3\pi}{4}\right) + 5 \sin\left(\frac{3\pi}{4}\right)$$
$$\frac{3\sqrt{2}}{2} = \frac{A\sqrt{2}}{2} + \frac{5\sqrt{2}}{2}$$
$$A = 2$$

Hence $x = 2 \cos 4t + 5 \sin 4t$

(b) $x = 2 \cos 4t + 5 \sin 4t$
when $t = 0$, $x = 2 \cos 0 + 5 \sin 0 = 2$

(c) $\dfrac{dx}{dt} = -8 \sin 4t + 20 \cos 4t$

When $t = 0$, $\dfrac{dx}{dt} = 20$, so the initial speed is 20 m s^{-1}.

(d) when $x = 2$, $v = 20$, so using $v^2 = \omega^2(a^2 - x^2)$ gives
$$400 = 16(a^2 - 4)$$
$$25 = a^2 - 4$$
$$a = \sqrt{29} \text{ m}$$

EXERCISE 6A

1 A piston executes SHM at the rate of 50 cycles per minute, between two fixed points 0.1 m apart. Find the maximum speed and maximum acceleration of the piston.

2 A sewing machine needle executes SHM about a fixed point O. When the particle is 2 cm from O its acceleration is 8 m s^{-2}. Find the period of the motion.

3 A particle moves with simple harmonic motion between the two points A and B, which are 10 cm apart. The particle is moving at a speed of 2 m s^{-1}, when it is 2 cm from A.

   (a) Find the time that it takes the particle to move from A to B.

   (b) Find the maximum speed of the particle. [A]

4 A particle executes SHM about a fixed point. The maximum speed of the particle is 6 m s^{-1}, and its maximum acceleration is 18 m s^{-2}. Find the amplitude and period of the motion.

5 A particle P, executes SHM about a mean position O. When P is 25 cm from O its speed is 2 m s^{-1}, and when it is 50 cm from O its speed is 1 m s^{-1}. Find the amplitude and period of the motion.

6 The tip of a saw blade executes SHM between two fixed points, A and B, 10 cm apart. If the speed of the particle is 2 m s^{-1} when it is 1 cm from A, find the period of the motion.

7 A particle, P, executes SHM about a mean position O with amplitude a. How far from O is the kinetic energy of P half its maximum?

8 The blade of an electric saw moves up and down describing simple harmonic motion. The tip of the blade moves between two points a distance d apart. The amplitude, speed and period of the motion can all be varied.

(a) For one particular job the maximum speed of the blade is set to 5 m s^{-1} and d is set to 5 cm. Find the period of the motion.

(b) The maximum speed of the blade can be set to any value. Show that the speed of the blade always drops to half its maximum when it is at a distance of $\dfrac{d\sqrt{3}}{4}$ from the mid point of its motion. [A]

9 The motion of a piston in an engine can be modelled by simple harmonic motion, in which the centre of mass of the piston moves up and down between two points, 8 cm apart, on a vertical line. Assume that the period of the motion is 0.03 seconds. The mass of the piston is 200 grams.

(a) Show that the maximum speed of the piston is $\dfrac{8\pi}{3} \text{ m s}^{-1}$.

(b) Find the speed of the piston when it is 1 cm from its maximum height.

(c) When the piston is at its lowest point, find its acceleration and hence the magnitude of the resultant force acting on it.

(d) Assume that, when the piston is at its lowest point, it is acted on by the force of gravity and a single upward vertical force. Find the magnitude of the upward force, and comment on how significant it is to include gravity when modelling the forces acting on the piston. [A]

10 A particle, *P*, which executes SHM starts from its equilibrium position at time $t = 0$. The period of motion is *T* seconds. How long, in terms of *T*, does it take to travel half the amplitude?

11 A particle, *P*, executes SHM between two fixed points, *A* and *B*, a distance *2a* apart. The particle is initially at rest at *A*. The period of the motion is *T*. How far does the particle travel in times

    (a) $\dfrac{T}{8}$,   **(b)** $\dfrac{T}{4}$,   **(c)** $\dfrac{T}{2}$,   **(d)** $\dfrac{3T}{4}$,   **(e)** $\dfrac{7T}{8}$?

12 A spot of light moves with SHM. The amplitude of the motion is 10 m and its period is 20 s. The displacement of the spot from its central position, at time *t* seconds, is *x* m. Assume that initially $x = 0$.

    (a) Find an expression for *x* at time *t*.

    (b) Find the time taken for the spot to move directly from the point where $x = 5$ to the point where $x = 10$.

13 The height of a tide relative to its mean height is to be modelled as SHM with amplitude 8 m and period 12 hours, about its mean position *O*. When $t = 0$ it is high tide. Find *t* when the height of the tide is:

    (a) 2 m above *O* for the first time

    (b) for the second time

    (c) for the third time.

14 The graph shows how the displacement, *s*, of the tip of a needle in a sewing machine varies with time, *t*. The displacement, *s*, is measured from the level of the cloth in the machine.

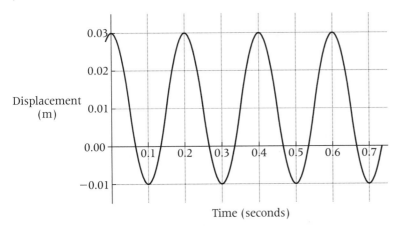

Assume that the motion of the tip of the needle is simple harmonic and that its displacement can be modelled by $s = A \cos(\omega t) + d$.

    (a) Find the values of *A*, ω and *d*.

    (b) Find the time when the needle first pierces the cloth.

    (c) Find the maximum speed of the needle and the speed when it pierces the cloth.   [A]

15 The height, x m, of a tide above its mean value, at time t hours is to be modelled by the equation,

$$x = A \cos \omega t + B \sin \omega t.$$

When $t = 0$, $x = 3$ and when $t = 2$, $x = 2$. The time between each high tide is 12 hours.

(a) Find the values of ω, A and B.

(b) Find t for the first high tide.

(c) Find t for the first low tide.

16 A saw blade moves up and down with simple harmonic motion as it cuts a board. The displacement of the tip of the blade varies between 2 and 7 cm below the board and is initially 7 cm. The blade completes 20 cycles per second.

(a) Find an expression for the displacement of the tip of the blade below the board at time t seconds.

(b) Find the time when the blade first reaches its maximum speed.

(c) Find the time when the blade first reaches half of its maximum speed.

17 A particle describes simple harmonic motion about a centre O. When at a distance of 5 cm from O its speed is 24 cm s^{-1} and when at a distance of 12 cm from O its speed is 10 cm s^{-1}. Find the period of the motion and the amplitude of the oscillation. Determine the time in seconds, to two decimal places, for the particle to travel a distance of 3 cm from O. [A]

18 A particle moves with simple harmonic motion along a straight line. At a certain instant it is 9 m away from the centre, O, of the motion and has a speed of 6 m s^{-1} and an acceleration of 2.25 m s^{-2}. Find

(a) the period of the motion

(b) the amplitude of the motion

(c) the greatest speed of the particle.

Given that at time $t = 0$, the particle is 7.5 m from O and is moving towards O, find its displacement from O at any subsequent time, t, and also find the time when it first passes through O. [A]

6.2 Forces producing simple harmonic motion

All the questions in this chapter so far, have given the information that a particle is performing simple harmonic motion. Once you know that a particle is performing SHM then you can use all the equations derived in the previous section. However, you need to be able to prove that the particle is performing SHM, by considering the resultant force on it. The goal in every proof of SHM is to end up showing that the acceleration is proportional to displacement and in the opposite direction to the displacement (which of course is the definition of SHM), i.e.

$$\frac{d^2x}{dt^2} = -\omega^2 x$$

Note: the negative sign here, is vital. Examiners usually punish its omission heavily.

When considering the resultant force on the particle, it will be necessary to write it in terms of its displacement from an origin. The origin is usually the point where the resultant force on the particle is zero. This will be the equilibrium position of the motion.

When approach problems of this type, follow the strategy listed below.

(a) Draw a force diagram.

(b) Express each force in terms of x the displacement from the equilibrium position.

(c) Apply Newton's second law.

Worked example 6.7

In this question take $g = 10\,\text{m s}^{-2}$.

A particle of mass 2 kg is connected to a light spring of natural length 0.5 m and modulus of elasticity 40 N. One end of the spring is attached to a fixed point and the particle hangs in equilibrium.

(a) Find the extension in the spring when the particle is hanging in this position.

The particle is then pulled a distance of 20 cm downwards and released.

(b) Show that the motion of the particle is simple harmonic, and find the period of the motion.

(c) Find the distance that the particle travels in the first tenth of a second after being released.

Solution

(a) In equilibrium the tension will be equal to the weight:

$$T = 2g$$

You will need to use Hooke's law which states that $T = \dfrac{\lambda e}{l}$, where λ is the modulus of elasticity, e the extension of the string and l the natural length of the string.

Using Hooke's law gives,

$$T = \frac{40e}{0.5}$$

$$2g = \frac{40e}{0.5}$$

$$e = 25 \text{ cm}$$

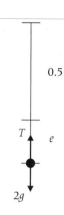

(b) The equilibrium position is now chosen as the origin and you must consider the resultant force on the particle when displaced x from here.

First consider the tension in the spring. Note that the total extension of the spring is $x + 0.25$. Then using Hooke's law

$$T = \frac{40(x + 0.25)}{0.5}$$

Then taking account of the weight the resultant force on the particle is

$$2g - T = 20 - \frac{40(x + 0.25)}{0.5}$$

Now apply $F = ma$, to give

$$2\frac{d^2x}{dt^2} = 20 - \frac{40(x + 0.25)}{0.5}$$

$$= -80x$$

$$\frac{d^2x}{dt^2} = -40x$$

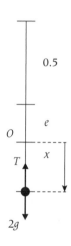

Note: the positive direction of the resultant force must always be the direction in which x increases.

This shows that the particle performs SHM. Note that $\omega^2 = 40$, which can then be used to find the period of the motion.

$$\text{Period} = \frac{2\pi}{\omega} = \frac{2\pi}{\sqrt{40}} = 0.993 \text{ s}.$$

(c) When the particle is first released its speed is zero, which means that it is released from one of its extreme positions. So the displacement will be of the form $x = A \cos(\omega t)$.

As the particle is a maximum of 0.2 m from its equilibrium position, the amplitude of the motion will be 0.2 m, so: $A = 0.2$

So the displacement is given by,

$$x = 0.2 \cos \sqrt{40}t$$

When $t = 0.1$, $x = 0.2 \cos \sqrt{40} \times 0.1 = 0.161$ m
Hence the distance travelled by the particle is

$$0.2 - 0.161 = 0.039 \text{ m}$$
$$= 3.9 \text{ cm}.$$

Knowing where the equilibrium position is situated is important when answering questions on SHM. However it does not have to be known when proving SHM, as the next worked example demonstrates.

Worked example 6.8

A sphere, of mass m kg, is supported by a spring as shown in the diagram. The spring has natural length l and modulus of elasticity λ.

(a) Find the extension of the spring when the sphere is in equilibrium.

(b) Find the tension in the spring when the sphere is displaced x m below the equilibrium position.

(c) Show that the motion is simple harmonic and find the period.

Solution

(a) In equilibrium the tension is equal to the weight of the sphere. Using Hooke's law gives

$$mg = \frac{\lambda e}{l}$$

$$e = \frac{mgl}{\lambda}$$

(b) When the sphere is displaced x m from its equilibrium position, the total extension of the spring is $x + \dfrac{mgl}{\lambda}$.
Hence the tension in the spring can be found using Hooke's law

$$T = \frac{\lambda}{l}\left(x + \frac{mgl}{\lambda}\right)$$

$$= \frac{\lambda x}{l} + mg$$

(c) The resultant force on the sphere is

$$mg - T = mg - \left(\frac{\lambda x}{l} + mg \right)$$

$$= -\frac{\lambda x}{l}$$

Now using Newton's second law, $F = ma$ gives

$$m\frac{d^2x}{dt^2} = -\frac{\lambda x}{l}$$

$$\frac{d^2x}{dt^2} = -\frac{\lambda}{lm}x$$

So you have simple harmonic motion, with $\omega = \sqrt{\dfrac{\lambda}{lm}}$.

The period can now be found

$$\text{Period} = \frac{2\pi}{\omega}$$

$$= 2\pi \sqrt{\frac{lm}{\lambda}}$$

Worked example 6.9

A light elastic string, with a natural length of 2.5 m and modulus 15 N, is stretched between two points, A and B, which are 3 m apart on a smooth horizontal table. A particle, P, of mass 3 kg is attached to the mid-point of the string. The particle is pulled 8 cm towards B and then released.

(a) Show that the particle moves with simple harmonic motion.

(b) Find the speed of the particle when it is 155 cm from A.

Solution

Let O be the centre of AB, and let $x = 0$ at this point.

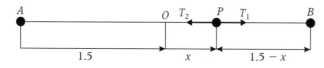

The above diagram shows the forces on the particle when it has been displaced x m from O.

(The weight of the particle and the normal reaction between the table and the particle have not been included, as they are in equilibrium and are perpendicular to the motion.)

(a) To find the tensions in each side of the string (T_1 and T_2) we need to use Hooke's law. When doing this you can consider each side, AP and BP, as a separate elastic string of natural length 1.25 m and modulus of elasticity 15 N.

$$T_1 = \frac{15(0.25 - x)}{1.25}$$
$$T_2 = \frac{15(0.25 + x)}{1.25}$$

The resultant force on the particle will be $T_1 - T_2$.

Applying $F = ma$ gives

$$3\ddot{x} = T_1 - T_2 = \frac{15(0.25 - x)}{1.25} - \frac{15(0.25 + x)}{1.25}$$
$$\therefore \ddot{x} = -8x$$

This equation shows that the particle executes SHM, with equilibrium position O.

(b) Initially the particle is released 8 cm from O: That is with $v = 0$, when $x = 0.08$. Hence the amplitude is 0.08 m. When the particle is 155 cm from A, $x = 0.05$.

Applying

$$v^2 = \omega^2(a^2 - x^2) \text{ gives}$$
$$v^2 = 8(0.08^2 - 0.05^2)$$
$$v = 0.177 \text{ m s}^{-1}.$$

EXERCISE 6B

1 A particle, P, of mass 400 grams, is suspended from a fixed point, A, by a light elastic string of natural length 50 cm. The particle is initially hanging in equilibrium below A. The length is 60 cm in this position.

(a) Find the modulus of elasticity of the string.

The particle is then pulled 10 cm downwards and released.

(b) Find the tension in the string in terms of x, the displacement in metres of the particle from its equilibrium position.

(c) Show that P executes SHM and find its maximum speed.

2 A light elastic spring, of natural length 40 cm and modulus of elasticity 20 N, has one end fixed at a point A on a smooth horizontal table. A sphere, S, of mass 500 grams is attached to the other and of the spring. Initially the sphere is released from rest at B, a point on the table where $AB = 50$ cm.

(a) Calculate the initial acceleration of the sphere.

(b) Show that the subsequent motion of S is simple harmonic.

(c) Find the period of the motion.

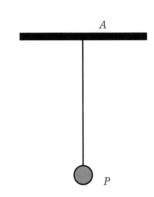

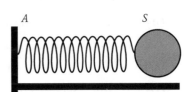

3 A particle, of mass 200 grams, is suspended from a fixed point A, by a light, elastic string of natural length 50 cm, and modulus of elasticity 4.9 N.The particle is initially hanging in equilibrium below A.

(a) Find the extension in the string when the particle is in equilibrium.

The particle is now pulled downwards and released from rest below the equilibrium position.

(b) Show that the ensuing motion is simple harmonic, provided that the initial displacement is not too great.

(c) Find the maximum initial displacement for which the subsequent motion will be simple harmonic.

(d) Find the time when the particle reaches its equilibrium position for the first time.

4 A student sets up an experiment where a 40 gram mass is attached to a spring of length 50 cm and modulus of elasticity 50 N as shown in the diagram. Assume that the surface is horizontal, that there is no friction and that the mass is initially at rest.

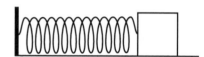

The mass is set into motion by moving it 1 cm to one side of its equilibrium position and releasing it.

(a) Find the magnitude of the tension in the spring when the extension of the spring is 1 cm.

(b) Show that $\dfrac{d^2x}{dt^2} = -2500x$, where x is the extension of the spring.

(c) Find the period of the oscillations and the maximum speed of the mass.

(d) The student sets the mass into motion and tries to confirm his calculation for the period of the oscillations. What difficulty might he encounter? [A]

5 An elastic rope has natural length 20 cm and modulus of elasticity 40 N. One end of the rope is attached to a fixed point and a particle, of mass 200 grams, hangs from the other end.

(a) Find the extension of the rope when the mass is at rest.

Assume that when the mass moves, it always travels along a vertical line that passes through the point of suspension.

(b) At time t seconds, the displacement of the mass from its equilibrium position is x metres. Find the tension in the rope in terms of x, and show that $\dfrac{d^2x}{dt^2} = -1000x$.

(c) The mass is set in motion from its equilibrium position, so that it has an initial upward speed of $U \, \mathrm{m \, s^{-1}}$. Find the maximum value of U for which simple harmonic motion will take place.

(d) Explain why in reality
   (i) the mass could be set in motion with a greater initial speed, without the rope becoming slack
   (ii) an even greater initial speed could be used if the mass initially moves downwards. [A]

6 A baby bouncer consists of a length of elastic, of modulus of elasticity λ, that is attached to a fixed point and to a harness, in which a baby sits. The baby then enjoys the sensation of moving up and down. It is important in designing a baby bouncer to produce simple harmonic motion of an appropriate frequency.

A model of the baby bouncer assumes that the elastic of natural length, l, is attached to a baby. The baby is modelled as a particle of mass m. The other end of the elastic is fixed to a point directly above the baby.

(a) Find the extension of the elastic if the baby is at rest.

The baby is pulled down a certain distance and released from rest, to start the motion.

(b) Show that the motion of the baby is described by the differential equation
$$\frac{d^2x}{dt^2} = -\frac{\lambda x}{ml},$$
where x is the displacement of the baby from the equilibrium position at time t. Find the period of the motion and state the maximum initial displacement if simple harmonic motion is to take place.

(c) Find the length of elastic that should be used to obtain the same period with a baby of mass M. As their baby becomes heavier, describe how a parent should adjust the length of the elastic to give simple harmonic motion of the same period. [A]

7 A light elastic spring, of modulus $8mg$ and natural length l, has one end attached to a ceiling and carries a scale pan of mass m at the other end. The scale pan is given a vertical displacement from its equilibrium position and released to oscillate with period T.

Prove that $T = 2\pi\sqrt{\dfrac{l}{8g}}$.

A weight of mass km is placed in the scale pan and from the new equilibrium position the procedure is repeated. The period of oscillation is now $2T$. Find the value of k. Find also the maximum amplitude of the latter oscillations if the weight and scale pan do not separate during the motion. [A]

8 An elastic string, of natural length 1 m and modulus 2 N, is stretched between two points A and B on a smooth horizontal table, where $AB = 2$ m. A particle P, of mass 500 grams, is attached to the mid-point of the string. The particle is released from rest at C where C is a point on the table where $BC = 75$ cm. Show that subsequently the particle performs SHM, and find the period of the motion.

9 A light elastic string, of natural length 40 cm and modulus of elasticity 1 N, is stretched between two fixed points, A and B, on a smooth horizontal table, where $AB = 60$ cm. A particle, P, of mass 100 grams, is attached to the mid-point of the string and is projected towards B with speed 0.5 m s^{-1} from the mid point of AB. Show that the subsequent motion is simple harmonic, and find the amplitude and period of the motion.

10 Three points O,B,C lie in that order, on a straight line l on a smooth horizontal plane with $OB = 0.3$ m and $OC = 0.4$ m. A particle, P, describes simple harmonic motion with centre O along the line l. At B the speed of the particle is 12 m s^{-1} and at C its speed is 9 m s^{-1}. Find

(a) the amplitude of the motion

(b) the period of the motion

(c) the maximum speed of P

(d) the time to travel from O to C.

11 The simple harmonic motion in question **10**, is caused by a light elastic spring attached to P. The other end of the spring is fixed at a point A on l where A is on the opposite side of O to B and C, and $AO = 2$ m. Given that P has mass 0.2 kg, find the modulus of elasticity of the spring, and the energy stored in it when $AP = 2.4$ m. [A]

12 A particle of mass m, is attached at the point C, to two light elastic strings AC and BC. The other ends of the strings are attached to two fixed points, A and B, on a smooth horizontal table, where $AB = 4a$. Both of the strings have the same natural length, a, and the same modulus. When the particle is in its equilibrium position the tension in each string is mg. Show that when the particle performs oscillations along the line AB in which neither string slackens, the motion is simple harmonic with period $\pi\sqrt{\dfrac{2a}{g}}$.

The breaking tension in each string has magnitude $\dfrac{3mg}{2}$.

Show that when the particle is performing complete simple harmonic oscillations the amplitude of the motion must be less than $\frac{1}{2}a$. Given that the amplitude of the simple harmonic oscillations is $\frac{1}{4}a$, find the maximum speed of the particle. [A]

Key point summary

1 For simple harmonic motion to take place   *p129*

$$\frac{d^2x}{dt^2} = -\omega^2 x.$$

2 Velocity v decreases as displacement x increases   *p129*
giving $v^2 = \omega^2(a^2 - x^2)$.

3 The amplitude, often referred to as a, is the greatest *p130*
distance of the body describing SHM, from the central
position of the body.

4 Period of motion $= \dfrac{2\pi}{\omega}$ *p131*

5 Displacement of a body describing SHM, can be   *p131*
expressed in one of the following forms:

$x = A \sin \omega t$

$x = A \cos \omega t$

$x = A \cos \omega t + B \sin \omega t$

Test yourself	**What to review**

1 A particle moves with SHM between two points that are 9 cm apart. The period of the motion is 0.8 seconds.

Section 6.1

   (a) Find the maximum speed of the particle.

   (b) Find the speed of the particle when it is 2 cm from one of its extreme positions.

   (c) Find the maximum acceleration of the particle.

2 A mass suspended from a spring moves with simple harmonic motion. The period of the motion is 0.2 seconds and its amplitude is 6 cm. Initially the mass is at its equilibrium position and moving downwards.

Section 6.1

   (a) Find the initial speed of the mass.

   (b) Find an expression for the displacement of the mass at time t seconds.

   (c) Find the time that it takes for the mass to move 2 cm from its equilibrium position.

   (d) Find the time when the mass is 3 cm above the equilibrium position for the first time.

3 A sphere, of mass 400 grams, is attached to one end of a spring that has its other end attached to a fixed point. The spring has natural length 50 cm and modulus of elasticity 40 N.

Section 6.2

   (a) Find the length of the spring when the sphere is in equilibrium.

The sphere is pulled down from its equilibrium position and released from rest.

   (b) Find the tension in the spring, when the sphere is x m below the equilibrium position.

   (c) Show that the sphere moves with simple harmonic motion and find the period of the motion.

Test yourself ANSWERS

3 (a) 4.9 cm,   **(b)** $T = 3.92 + 80x$,   **(c)** 0.444 s.

2 (a) 0.188 m s^{-1},   **(b)** $x = 0.06 \sin (10\pi t)$,   **(c)** 0.0108 s,   **(d)** 0.117 s.

1 (a) 0.353 m s^{-1},   **(b)** 0.294 m s^{-1},   **(c)** 2.78 m s^{-2}.

Exam style practice paper

Time allowed 1 hour 45 minutes

Maximum marks: 80

Answer **all** questions

1 An aeroplane has position vector **r** metres relative the point O at time t seconds.

   $$\mathbf{r} = (200 + 50t)\mathbf{i} + (30 - 0.5t^2)\mathbf{j} + 0.8t^2\mathbf{k}$$

   The unit vectors **i**, **j** and **k** are directed east, north and vertically upwards, respectively.

   (a) Find the distance of the aeroplane from O when $t = 10$.   *(2 marks)*

   (b) Find an expression for the velocity of the aeroplane at time t.   *(2 marks)*

   (c) Find the time when the aeroplane is rising at 20 m s^{-1}.   *(2 marks)*

   (d) Find the time when the aeroplane is travelling south east.   *(2 marks)*

2 In a bungee running contest an elastic rope has one end fixed at O. A competitor, of mass 60 kg, is attached to the other end of the rope. The competitor runs to the point A, 10 metres from O, where he is brought to rest by the rope. The rope has natural length 5 m and modulus of elasticity 400 N.

   (a) Calculate the elastic potential energy in the rope when the competitor is at A.   *(2 marks)*

   At A the competitor falls over and is dragged back by the elastic rope. The coefficient of friction between the competitor and the ground is 0.3.

   (b) Find the speed of the competitor when the rope becomes slack.   *(3 marks)*

   (c) Find the distance of the competitor from O when he comes to rest.   *(3 marks)*

3 A particle moves with simple harmonic motion. Its maximum speed is 5 m s^{-1} and its maximum acceleration is 100 m s^{-2}.

   (a) Show that the period of the motion is $\dfrac{\pi}{10}$ s.   *(3 marks)*

   (b) Find the time that it takes for the speed of the particle to increase from 1 m s^{-1} to 2 m s^{-1}.   *(4 marks)*

4 A uniform lamina is bounded by the curve $y = 5x - x^2$ and the x axis.

   (a) Show that the area of the lamina is $\dfrac{125}{6}$ square units.   *(3 marks)*

   (b) Find the coordinates of the centre of mass of the lamina.   *(6 marks)*

The lamina is suspended from one end of its straight edge.

   (c) Find the angle between the straight edge and the vertical.   *(2 marks)*

5 A lorry has a mass of 40 tonnes and a power output of 400 kW. It ascends a slope inclined at $5°$ to the horizontal at a maximum speed of 10 m s^{-1}.

   (a) Show that the magnitude of the resistance force acting on the lorry when it travels at 10 m s^{-1} is approximately 5830 N.   *(3 marks)*

Two possible models for the magnitude of the resistance are to be considered.

The first assumes that the resistance forces are proportional to the speed of the lorry.

The second assumes that the resistance forces are proportional to the square of the speed of the lorry.

   (b) For each model predict the maximum speed of the lorry on a horizontal road, correct to two significant figures.   *(4 marks)*

   (c) State which of the models is more realistic. Explain why.   *(2 marks)*

6 A particle, of mass m, is attached to two strings. The other ends of the strings are attached at the points A and B, which is directly above A. The particle describes a horizontal circle, of radius r, with A at its centre. The angle between the two strings is 45°.

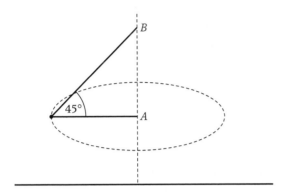

(a) Find the tension in the upper string in terms of m and g. *(4 marks)*

(b) Show that the tension in the lower string is $m\left(\dfrac{v^2}{r}-g\right)$

and state the range of values of v for which this expression is true. *(4 marks)*

(c) Find the speed of the particle, in terms of r and g, when the tensions in the two strings are equal. *(3 marks)*

When the tensions in the two strings are equal they are released, so that the particle is free to move under gravity only. The point A is a distance $\sqrt{2}r$ above ground level.

(d) Show that the speed of the particle when it hits the ground is $rg\sqrt{(1+3\sqrt{2})}$. *(4 marks)*

7 A ball, of mass 200 grams, is projected vertically upwards with an initial velocity of 8 m s^{-1}. When it moves, at a speed of $v\text{ m s}^{-1}$, it is subject to a resistance force of magnitude $\dfrac{v}{50}\text{ N}$.

(a) Show that it takes the ball approximately 0.785 seconds to reach its maximum height. *(6 marks)*

(b) Find the maximum height of the ball. *(6 marks)*

8 A sphere, of mass 0.2 kg, is attached to one end of an elastic string of length 0.5 m and modulus of elasticity 20 N. The other end of the string is fixed. Initially the sphere hangs in equilibrium, directly below the fixed end of the string.

(a) Calculate the extension of the string, when the sphere is in equilibrium. *(2 marks)*

The sphere is pulled downwards from its equilibrium position and released. At time t seconds its displacement is x metres below its equilibrium position.

(b) Show that $\dfrac{dx^2}{dt^2} = -200x$. *(4 marks)*

The sphere is released from rest 0.1 metres below its equilibrium position.

(c) Find the speed of the sphere when it has been moving for 2 seconds. *(4 marks)*

Answers

1 Kinematics and variable acceleration

EXERCISE 1A

1 **(a)** $83\frac{1}{3}$ m, **(b)** $v = \dfrac{t^2}{2} - \dfrac{t^3}{30}$, **(c)** $a = t - \dfrac{t^2}{10}$,

  (d) Increases from 0 initially, to a maximum at $t = 5$ and then decreases to 0 when $t = 10$.

2 **(a)** $v = 2t - \dfrac{t^2}{20}$, $a = 2 - \dfrac{t}{10}$,

  (b) $t = 20$,

  (c) 20 m s^{-1},

  (d) 267 m.

3 **(a)** Lift comes to rest,

  (b)

4 **(a)** $0 \leqslant t \leqslant 15$,

  (b) 112.5 m,

  (c)

5 243 m.

6 (a) $v = 0.2 \cos (0.5t)$,   **(b)** $0.2 \, \text{m s}^{-1}$,

   (c) $-0.0841 \, \text{m s}^{-2}$,   **(d)** $-0.1 \leqslant a \leqslant 0.1 \, \text{m s}^{-2}$.

7 (a) 0,   **(b)** $0 \leqslant t \leqslant 800\pi$,

   (c) 300 m,   **(d)** $0.000\,234 \, \text{m s}^{-2}$.

8 (a) $A = 15$,   **(b)** $k = \dfrac{4}{3}$,

   (c)

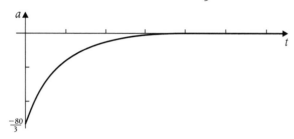

9 (a) 4 m,   **(b)** $6 \, \text{m s}^{-1}$.

10 (a) $0 \, \text{m s}^{-1}$, $40 \, \text{m s}^{-1}$,

    (b)

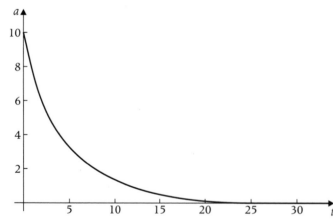

11 (b) $-(kU + g)$

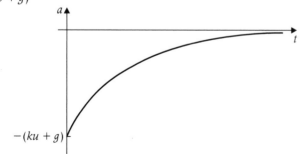

12 (a) $v = 5t - \dfrac{t^3}{5}, a = 5 - \dfrac{3t^2}{5}$,   **(b)** $0 \leqslant t \leqslant 5$, 31.25 m,

   (c) Decreases to -10, 9.62 m s^{-1},

   (d) Falls from rest, no air resistance.

EXERCISE 1B

1 (a) $v = \dfrac{t^3}{300}$,   **(b)** $\dfrac{5}{12}$ m s^{-1},   **(c)** $\dfrac{25}{48}$ m.

2 20 m s^{-1}, 267 m.

3 38.3 m.

4 11.1 m s^{-1}, 42.1 m.

5 (b) 17.5 m s^{-1},   **(c)** 183 m.

6 (a) $v = 2t - \dfrac{t^2}{20}$,   **(b)** $t = 20$ s, $v = 20$ m s^{-1},

   (c) Speeds up for first 20 s and slows down for last 10 s,

   (d) 450 m.

7 (a) $a = 1.8 \cos (3t)$, **(b)** $x = 1 - 0.2 \cos (3t)$,

   (c)

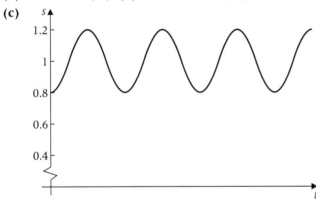

8 (a) $v = 4.9(1 - e^{-2t})$, $s = 2.45e^{-2t} + 4.9t - 2.45$,

   (b)   **(c)** 95.6 m.

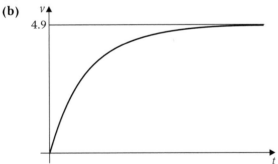

9 18.7 m.

10 (a) $v = \dfrac{2}{5\pi} \sin (100\pi t)$,   **(b)** $\dfrac{2}{5\pi} = 0.127$ m s^{-1},

   (c) 0.000 405 m.

11 (a) $x = \dfrac{3}{2} - \dfrac{3}{2} \cos (2t) - \sin (2t)$,   **(b)** $\sqrt{13}$ m s^{-1}.

EXERCISE 1C

1 (a) $\mathbf{v} = 2t\mathbf{i} + (12t - 1)\mathbf{j}$, $\mathbf{a} = 2\mathbf{i} + 12\mathbf{j}$,
  (b) $\mathbf{r} = 11\mathbf{i} + 96\mathbf{j}$, $\mathbf{v} = 8\mathbf{i} + 47\mathbf{j}$.

2 (a) $\mathbf{v}_A = 30\mathbf{i} + (6t - 120)\mathbf{j}$, $\mathbf{v}_B = 20\mathbf{i} + 40\mathbf{j}$,
  (b) $v_B = 44.7 \text{ m s}^{-1}$,
  (c) $t = 30$, 756 m.

3 $\mathbf{v} = 2t\mathbf{i} + 2\mathbf{j}$, $\mathbf{a} = 2\mathbf{i}$.

4 (a) $\mathbf{v} = \left(4 - \dfrac{2t}{5}\right)\mathbf{i} + 10\mathbf{j}$,   (b) $t = 20$, 200 m,
  (c) $t = 10$, 10 m s^{-1},   (d) $\dfrac{2}{5} \text{ m s}^{-1}$ due west.

5 (a) $\mathbf{v} = (2t - 8)\mathbf{i} + (6t^2 - 10t + 6)\mathbf{j}$,
  (b) $\mathbf{F} = 6\mathbf{i} + (36t - 30)\mathbf{j}$,
  (c) $t = 4$, $-14\mathbf{i} + 72\mathbf{j}$.

6 (a) $t = 2$, $v = 20.2 \text{ m s}^{-1}$,   (b) $t = 5$, $\mathbf{a} = -\mathbf{j}$.

7 $38.3\mathbf{i} + 16.7\mathbf{j}$.

8 (a) 3.2 kg,   (b) $28.3\mathbf{i} + 46.9\mathbf{j}$.

9 $\mathbf{v} = (2 + t)\mathbf{i} + (5 + 0.1t^2)\mathbf{j}$, $\mathbf{r} = \left(2t + \dfrac{t^2}{2}\right)\mathbf{i} + \left(5t + \dfrac{t^3}{30}\right)\mathbf{j}$.

10 (a) $\mathbf{v} = (3 + t^2)\mathbf{i} + \left(6 - \dfrac{5t^2}{2}\right)\mathbf{j}$,   (b) $\mathbf{r} = \left(3t + \dfrac{t^3}{3}\right)\mathbf{i} + \left(6t - \dfrac{5t^3}{6}\right)\mathbf{j}$.

11 (a) $\mathbf{v} = 4t\mathbf{i} - \dfrac{t^2}{2}\mathbf{j}$,   (b) $\mathbf{r} = (5 + 2t^2)\mathbf{i} - \left(10 + \dfrac{t^3}{6}\right)\mathbf{j}$.

12 32 m s^{-1}, 256 m s^{-2}.

13 (a) $-4\mathbf{i} + 0\mathbf{j}$, $0\mathbf{i} - 6\mathbf{j}$, $16\mathbf{i} + 0\mathbf{j}$,   (b) 16 m s^{-2}, 12 m s^{-2}.

14 (a) 3 m s^{-2} upwards,
  (b) (i) $4\mathbf{i} + 6\mathbf{j} + 6\mathbf{k}$,   (ii) 9.38 m s^{-2},
  (c) $39.8°$ above horizontal.

15 (a) 20 m s^{-1}, 20 m s^{-1}, 20 m s^{-1}, speed is constant,
  (b) $100\mathbf{i} + 200\mathbf{j} + 0\mathbf{k}$, $100\mathbf{i} + 210\mathbf{j} + 0\mathbf{k}$, 10.5 m.

16 $t = 0$, $t = \pi$.

17 (a) A $0\mathbf{i} + 0\mathbf{j}$, $20\mathbf{i} - 1.6\mathbf{j}$ B $0\mathbf{i} + 0\mathbf{j}$, $20\mathbf{i} - 0\mathbf{j}$
          $100\mathbf{i} - 4\mathbf{j}$, $20\mathbf{i} + 0\mathbf{j}$ $100\mathbf{i} - 4\mathbf{j}$, $20\mathbf{i} + 0\mathbf{j}$
          $200\mathbf{i} + 0\mathbf{j}$, $20\mathbf{i} + 1.6\mathbf{j}$ $200\mathbf{i} + 0\mathbf{j}$, $20\mathbf{i} + 0\mathbf{j}$

  (b) Model **B** is better as the car will not leave the road when overtaking is complete or start and finish velocities are parallel to the road.

18 (a) $\mathbf{v} = 25\mathbf{i} + 5\sin\left(\dfrac{\pi t}{10}\right)\mathbf{j}$, **(b)** $v = 5\sqrt{25 + \sin^2\left(\dfrac{\pi t}{10}\right)}$,

(c) Max speed when $t = 5, 15$. Min speed when $t = 0, 10, 20$.
Speed increases and decreases while going up.
Speed increases and decreases while going down.

(d) Would expect speed to decrease on way up and increase on way down.

2 Energy

EXERCISE 2A

1 4.8 J.

2 3.75×10^{10} J.

3 3.6 J, 14.4 J.

4 4 725 000 J.

5 (a) $28\,\text{m s}^{-1}$, **(b)** 19.6 J.

6 (a) $7.68\,\text{m s}^{-1}$, **(b)** 1750 J.

EXERCISE 2B

1 (a) 320 000 J,
(b) (i) 320 000 J, $25.3\,\text{m s}^{-1}$,
(ii) 324 500 J, $25.5\,\text{m s}^{-1}$.

2 (a) 50 J, **(b)** 50 J, **(c)** 16.7 N.

3 (a) 62.72 J, $7.92\,\text{m s}^{-1}$, **(b)** 30.72 J, $5.54\,\text{m s}^{-1}$.

4 (a) 25 000 J, **(b)** 16 J, **(c)** 24 984 J, **(d)** 499.68 N.

5 0.8575 J, 56.25 cm.

6 (a) 1 340 000 J, $46.3\,\text{m s}^{-1}$, **(b)** 777 500 J, 1555 N.

7 (a) 300 000 J, **(b)** 235 200 J, **(c)** 64800 J, **(d)** 20 m,
(e) air resistance is not constant, usually some function of speed: the effect would be a greater stopping distance.

8 (a) 432 J, 108 N, **(b)** 1548 N.

9 (a) 249.9 N, **(b)** 1.45 cm.

10 48 N, $98.0\,\text{m s}^{-1}$.

EXERCISE 2C

1 (a) 2450 J,   (b) 9.90 m s^{-1}.

2 (a) 54 J,   (b) 6.89 m.

3 (a) 416 J,   (b) 440 J, 17.1 m s^{-1},   (c) 15.1 m s^{-1}.

4 (a) 630 J,   (b) 750 J, 5.00 m s^{-1},   (c) 1.28 m.

5 21.6 J,   (b) 19.2 J,   (c) 6.53 m.

6 (a) 32 400 J,   (b) 20 640 J,   (c) 12.7 m s^{-1}.

7 286 J, 6.90 m s^{-1}.

8 (a) 37 800 J,   (b) 1890 N,   (c) 13.2 m.

9 98 700 J, 13.4 m s^{-1}.

10 (a) 2695 J, 9.90 m s^{-1},   (b) 9.46 m s^{-1},   (c) 80.5°.

11 (a) 1728 J, 6.57 m s^{-1}, no air resistance,
   (b) 2.20 m,   (c) perpendicular to direction of motion.

12 (a) 431 N,   (b) 25.7 m,
   (c) use a variable resistance force, model the roller coaster as a
       number of connected particles.

EXERCISE 2D

1 (a) 0.392 m,   (b) 0.235 m,   (c) 0.0392 m.

2 0.5 m.

3 156.8 N .

4 68.0 grams.

5 (a) 0.392 cm,   (b) 0.196 cm,   (c) 0.784 cm.

EXERCISE 2E

1 (a) 0.8 J,   (b) 2.4 J.

2 7.07 m s^{-1}.

3 2.21 m s^{-1}.

5 (a) 1.28 m s^{-1},   (b) 16.7 cm.

6 40.5 cm, 2.21 m s^{-1}.

7 $\lambda = \dfrac{3mg}{2}$.

8 (a) $v = \sqrt{\dfrac{800 - 70\,875x^2}{162}}$,   (b) 10.6 cm.

9 (a) 0.196 cm, **(b)** 11.2 cm.

10 50.8 cm.

11 0.657 m s^{-1}.

12 3.32 m s^{-1}, 0.963 m.

13 7.07 m s^{-1}.

14 $\sqrt{2ga}$, $\sqrt{6ga}$.

15 (a) $9\sqrt{\dfrac{ga}{80}}$, **(b)** $\dfrac{5a}{4}$.

EXERCISE 2F

1 669 N.

2 1.64 m s^{-2}.

3 102 km.

4 (a) 785 N, **(b)** almost identical.

5 (a) 3.67×10^{24} N, **(b)** 3.67×10^{24} N.

EXERCISE 2G

1 3.08×10^{10} J.

2 (a) 7.38×10^{6} J, **(b)** yes, as values almost the same.

3 2.51×10^{9} J.

4 2.32×10^{6} J.

5 1.25×10^{11} J.

EXERCISE 2H

1 (a) 94 080 J, **(b)** 784 W.

2 100.8 W.

3 9×10^{5} W.

4 68.1 W.

5 (a) 900 N, **(b)** 675 N, **(c)** 0.525 m s^{-2}.

6 (a) $\dfrac{75v}{4}$, **(b)** 11 700 W, **(c)** 27.1 m s^{-1}.

7 31.2 m s^{-1}, 80.2 m s^{-1}.

8 (a) $\dfrac{400v}{27}$, **(b)** 37.2 m s^{-1}, **(c)** 54.5 m s^{-1}.

9 **(a)** $34.6 \, \text{m s}^{-1}$, **(b)** $24.5 \, \text{m s}^{-1}$.

10 **(a)** 200 N, **(b)** 427 000 J.

11, **(b)** $1.33 \, \text{m s}^{-1}$,

    (c) **(i)** motion very slow, so little air resistance,

        (ii) would accelerate for ever without air resistance.

12 **(a)** $30v$ N, **(b)** 19%,

    (c) small reduction leads to larger fuel savings, **(d)** $28.6 \, \text{m s}^{-1}$.

13 **(a)** 625 N, **(b)** $32.7 \, \text{m s}^{-1}$.

14 7500 W, $5 \, \text{m s}^{-2}$.

15 **(a)** **(b)** 50 000 W.

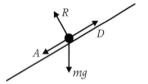

There are really 4 reaction forces.

3 Circular motion

EXERCISE 3A

1 **(a)** $\dfrac{1}{60}$ rpm, **(b)** $\dfrac{\pi}{1800}$ rad s^{-1}.

2 $\dfrac{\pi}{3}$ rad s^{-1}.

3 $51\,600 \, \text{m s}^{-1}$.

4 $2990 \, \text{m s}^{-1}$.

5 $52.4 \, \text{m s}^{-1}$, $13\,700 \, \text{m s}^{-2}$.

6 35.5 N.

7 2.5 m.

8 $1.54 \, \text{m s}^{-2}$.

9 $20.9 \, \text{m s}^{-1}$, $2190 \, \text{m s}^{-2}$.

10 **(a)** $\dfrac{\pi}{3}$ rad s^{-1}, **(b)** $\dfrac{2\pi}{3}$ m s^{-1}, $\dfrac{\pi}{2}$ m s^{-1}.

EXERCISE 3B

1 1750 N.

2 3.6 N towards the centre of the circle.

3 72 N.

4 $11.6 \, \text{m s}^{-1}$.

5 2 N.

6 576 N.

7 $2\pi\sqrt{\dfrac{a^3}{k}}$.

8 38.1 N.

9 3290 N, 0.336.

10 6.26 rad s^{-1}.

11 **(a)** Coin slides,　　　　**(b)** 4.4 cm,　　　　**(c)** No change.

12 0.227, 1.19m N.

13, **(b)** 6 m s^{-1},　　　　**(c)** 3 rad s^{-1},　　　　**(d)** 72 N.

14 0.340.

15 18.8 m s^{-1}.

16 1.98 rad s^{-1}.

17 **(a)** 49.3 m s^{-2}, 25.2 N,　**(b)** 0.639 s.

18 **(a)** 125 m s^{-2},　　　　**(b)** path is a tangent to the end of the strip.

19 0.33.

20 **(a)** 6000 N,　**(b)** $\mu \geqslant \dfrac{25}{49}$,　**(c)** 21.7 m s^{-1},　**(d)** air resistance.

21 **(a)**

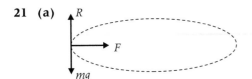

　　(b) 16.3 m　　　　**(c)**

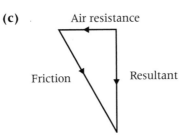

EXERCISE 3C

1 **(a)** 20.9 N, 4.57 rad s^{-1},　**(b)** 50 N, 66.9°,　**(c)** 0.272 m, 39.2 N.

2 20.0 N, 4.47 rad s^{-1}.

3 82.9 N, 65.5 cm.

4 **(a)** 48 N, **(b)** 35.2°, **(c)** 1.73 m.

5 56.6 N, 1.68 m s^{-1}.

6 2.56 rad s^{-1}.

7 0.959 rad s^{-1}.

8 $\sqrt{\dfrac{g\sqrt{3}}{r}}$.

9 $\dfrac{g}{l\omega^2}$.

10 $\dfrac{g}{2\pi^2}$.

11 $v = \dfrac{\sqrt{15ag}}{2}$, $R = 4mg$.

14 **(a)** 10 000 N, **(b)** $\alpha = \tan^{-1}\left(\dfrac{v^2}{rg}\right)$, $L = m\sqrt{\dfrac{v^4}{r^2} + g^2}$,
   (c) reduce r then α increases and L increases.

15 **(a) (i)** 453 N, **(ii)** 5.66 m s^{-2}, **(iii)** 3.36 m s^{-1},
   (b) 0.553 s, due to the actual size of the child,
   (c) 2.73 m, between 2 and 2.73 m from O.

16 **(a)** Light, inextensible, **(c)** 86.6 N, 52.0 N.

17, **(b)** $R = m\left(\dfrac{g}{\sqrt{2}} - \dfrac{v^2}{l}\right)$, **(c)** particle leaves contact with the cone.

18 **(a)** 19.7 m s^{-2}, **(b)** $R = 1380$ N, $F = 686$ N.

19 **(a)** $\tan \alpha = 5$, **(c)** $3.83 \leqslant v \leqslant 4.43$ m s^{-1},
   (d) 0.0735 J, **(e)** rotation of the coin.

EXERCISE 3D

1 34.2 m s^{-1}, 26.7°.

2 13.9 m s^{-1}.

4 25.0 m s^{-1}.

5 22.7 cm.

6 2770 N, 10 900 N, 0.254.

7 0.4, 21.8°, 35.2 m s^{-1}.

8 **(a)** 9600 N, **(b)** 9180 N.

EXERCISE 3E

1 **(a)** 3192 N, **(b)** 3198 N, **(c)** 3204 N.

2 910 N.

3 (a) 2020 N,

(b) When disc has rotated 57.8° from lowest position.

4 A 54 000 N.   B 33 200 N.   C 72 900 N.   D 68 700 N.

5 2.42 m s^{-1}.

4 Centres of mass by integration

EXERCISE 4A

1 (a) (8, 4),   **(b)** (7.5, 30),   **(c)** (0, 0.4),
(d) (0, 3.6),   **(e)** (6, 5).

2 (a) $\left(\dfrac{4}{5}, \dfrac{24}{7}\right)$,   **(b)** 13.1°.

3 (a) 1.6,   **(b)** symmetrical about $x = 0$,   **(c)** $\dfrac{4}{9}$,   **(d)** 66.0°.

5 $\left(\dfrac{\pi}{2} - 1, \dfrac{\pi}{8}\right)$.

6 76.0°.

7 60.9°.

8 (a) (6, 4),   **(b)** (6, 7).

9 (1, 2).

EXERCISE 4B

1 (a) $\left(\dfrac{7}{8}, 0\right)$,   **(b)** (2ln2, 0),   **(c)** $\left(\dfrac{155}{49}, 0\right)$,   **(d)** (1.54, 0).

2 (a) 18π,   **(b)** 4.5,   **(c)** 63.4°.

4 (a) $\dfrac{86}{31}$,   **(b)** 76.2°,   **(c)** 19.8°.

5, (b) Because symmetrical about $x = 2$.

6 (a) 1.97,   **(b)** 17.2°.

7 $\dfrac{3a}{20}$.

8 $\dfrac{11a^3\pi}{24}, \dfrac{5a^3\pi}{24}, \dfrac{21a}{88}, \dfrac{27a}{40}$.

9 (a) $\dfrac{5a}{8}$,   **(b)** 54.2°.

10 2.16.

EXERCISE 4C

2 **(a)** (2, 0),   **(b)** 80.5°.

3 **(a)** (4.64, 0),   **(b)** 11.5.

4 **(a)** (6.73, 0),   **(b)** 71.9°.

5 (13, 0).

6 8.89.

5 Application of differential equations in mechanics

EXERCISE 5A

1 **(a)** $v = 20e^{-2.5t}$,   **(b)** $s = 8(1 - e^{-2.5t})$,   **(c)** 8 m.

2 **(a)** $v = \dfrac{10}{5t + 2}$,   **(b)** $v = \dfrac{20}{10t + 1}$.

3 **(a)** $v = 80e^{-\frac{t}{2}}$,   **(b)** $s = 160(1 - e^{-\frac{t}{2}})$,   **(c)** 120 m.

4 **(a)** $v = 6 - 1.96t$,   **(b)** $v = 6e^{-2t}$,   **(c)** $v = 6.98e^{-2t} - 0.98$,

     (d) 5.02 m s^{-1}, 2.21 m s^{-1}, 0.159 m s^{-1},
     air resistance more significant than friction.

5 **(a)** $v = \dfrac{g}{4}(1 - e^{-4t})$,   **(b)** $s = \dfrac{g}{4}\left(t + \dfrac{1}{4}^{-4t}\right) - \dfrac{g}{16}$,   **(c)** 0.859 m.

6 $v = \dfrac{24}{5}(1 - e^{-\frac{t}{8}})$, $s = \dfrac{24}{5}t + \dfrac{192}{5}e^{-\frac{t}{8}} - \dfrac{192}{5}$.

7 **(a)** $v = \dfrac{g}{k}(1 - e^{-kt})$,   **(b)** $s = \dfrac{g}{k}\left(t + \dfrac{1}{k}e^{-kt} - \dfrac{1}{k}\right)$.

8 **(a)** 2 m s^{-1},   **(b)** $\dfrac{1}{4}\ln 3$.

9 **(a)** $\dfrac{7}{15}$ s,   **(b)** 3.18 m s^{-1}.

10 19.6 m s^{-1}, 2.90 s.

11 **(a)** Size of stone, type of fluid,

     (b) $x = \dfrac{g}{k}\left(t + \dfrac{1}{k}e^{-kt} - \dfrac{1}{k}\right)$,

     (c) $x_2 = \dfrac{g}{k}\left(t - 2 + \dfrac{1}{k}e^{-k(t-2)} - \dfrac{1}{k}\right)$, $d = \dfrac{2g}{k} + \dfrac{g}{k^2}(1 - e^{2k})e^{-kt}$,

     (d) tends to $\dfrac{2g}{k}$.

12 **(a)** 31.0 m s^{-1},   **(b)** 8.43 m s^{-1}.

EXERCISE 5B

1. **(a)** $v = 20 - \dfrac{x}{5}$, **(b)** 100 m.

2. 358 m.

3. 44.1 m s^{-1}.

4. 2.91 m s^{-1}.

5. **(c)** $c = \ln 27.45$, **(d)** 0.604 m.

6, **(d)** $c = 0.98 \ln 0.98$, **(e)** 0.0199 m.

7. $\dfrac{k}{2}\ln\!\left(1 + \dfrac{U^2}{gk}\right)$.

9. 4.43 m s^{-1}, 1.47 m.

10, **(c)** 6.67 s.

11. **(a)** Air resistance, friction,
    (b) $k = 24$, **(c)** 3.47 s.

12. **(a)** 32 m, **(b)** infinite distance,
    (c) model A, as it stops in a finite distance.

13. **(b)** $A = 20$, $c = -\dfrac{1}{20}$, **(c)** 18.5 m.

14. **(d)** Poor, important to include friction due to differences in stopping distances.

15. **(a)** Reasonable because it only falls approx. 2 cm,
    (b) 7.27 m s^{-1}, **(c)** 7.18 m s^{-1},
    (d) makes very little difference.

6 Simple harmonic motion

EXERCISE 6A

1. 0.262 m s^{-1}, 1.37 m s^{-2}.

2. 0.314 s.

3. **(a)** $\dfrac{\pi}{50}$, **(b)** 2.5 m s^{-1}.

4. 2 m, 2.09 s.

5. $\dfrac{\sqrt{5}}{4}$ m, $\dfrac{\pi}{2}$ s.

6. $\dfrac{3\pi}{100}$.

7. $\dfrac{a}{\sqrt{2}}$.

8. **(a)** $\dfrac{\pi}{100}$.

9 (b) 5.54 m s^{-1},   **(c)** 1755 m s^{-2}, 351 N,

  (d) 353 N, not at all significant.

10 $\dfrac{T}{12}$.

11 (a) $a\left(1 - \dfrac{1}{\sqrt{2}}\right)$,   **(b)** a,   **(c)** $2a$,   **(d)** $3a$ **(e)** $a\left(3 + \dfrac{1}{\sqrt{2}}\right)$.

12 (a) $x = 10 \sin\left(\dfrac{\pi t}{10}\right)$,   **(b)** $\dfrac{10}{3}$ s.

13 (a) 2.52 hours,   **(b)** 9.48 hours,   **(c)** 14.52 hours.

14 (a) $A = 0.02$, $\omega = 10\pi$, $d = 0.01$,

  (b) $t = \dfrac{1}{15}$ s,   **(c)** 0.628 m s^{-1}, 0.544 m s^{-1}.

15 (a) $\omega = \dfrac{\pi}{6}$, $A = 3$, $B = \dfrac{1}{\sqrt{3}}$,   **(b)** 0.363,   **(c)** 6.363.

16 (a) $x = 2.5 \cos(40\pi t) + 4.5$,   **(b)** $\dfrac{1}{80}$ s,   **(c)** $\dfrac{1}{240}$ s.

17 π s, 13 cm, 0.12 s.

18 (a) 4π s,   **(b)** 15 m,   **(c)** 7.5 m s^{-1}, $x = 15 \sin\left(\dfrac{t}{2} + \dfrac{5\pi}{6}\right)$, $\dfrac{\pi}{3}$ s.

EXERCISE 6B

1 (a) 19.6 N,   **(b)** $T = 3.92 + 39.2x$,   **(c)** 0.990 m s^{-1}.

2 (a) 10 m s^{-2},   **(c)** $\dfrac{\pi}{5}$ s.

3 (a) 0.2 m,   **(c)** 0.2 m,   **(d)** $\dfrac{\pi}{14}$ s.

4 (a) 1 N,   **(c)** $\dfrac{\pi}{25}$ s, 0.5 m s^{-1},   **(d)** too fast to count.

5 (a) 0.0098 m,   **(b)** $T = 200x + 1.96$,   **(c)** 0.310 m s^{-1},

  (d) (i) Energy lost due to air resistance, so greater initial speed,

    (ii) even more energy lost so an even greater initial speed.

6 (a) $\dfrac{mgl}{\lambda}$,   **(b)** $2\pi\sqrt{\dfrac{ml}{\lambda}}$, $\dfrac{mgl}{\lambda}$,

  (c) $\dfrac{ml}{M}$ decrease the length of the elastic.

7 $k = 3$, $\dfrac{l}{2}$.

8 $\dfrac{\pi}{2}$ s.

9 $\dfrac{\pi}{5}$ s, 0.05 m.

10 (a) $\dfrac{1}{2}$ m,   (b) $\dfrac{\pi}{15}$ s,   (c) $15\,\text{m s}^{-1}$,   (d) 0.0310 s.

11 360 N, 14.4 J.

12 $\sqrt{\dfrac{ga}{8}}$.

Answers to exam style practice paper

1 (a) 705 m,   (b) $\mathbf{v} = 50\mathbf{i} - t\mathbf{j} + 1.6t\mathbf{k}$,
    (c) 12.5 s,   (d) 50 s.

2 (a) 1000 J,   (b) $1.98\,\text{m s}^{-1}$,   (c) 4.33 m.

3 (b) 0.0105 s.

4 (b) (2.5, 2.5),   (c) 45°.

5 (a) $26\,\text{m s}^{-1}$,
    (c) first model as the top speed for the other is low.

6 (a) $\sqrt{2}mg$,   (b) $v \geqslant \sqrt{rg}$,   (c) $v \geqslant \sqrt{rg(1 + \sqrt{2})}$.

7 (b) 3.10 m.

8 (a) 4.9 cm,   (c) $0.0141\,\text{m s}^{-1}$.